George Micha...

COMPLETE

THE BIOGRAPHY

THE DISCOGRAPHY

THE LYRICS

THE MUSIC

THE INDEX

IMP

International
MUSIC
Publications

International Music Publications Limited
Griffin House 161 Hammersmith Road London W6 8BS England

CONTENTS

C000042590

This book © 2000 International Music Publications Limited
ISBN: 1–85909–870–3
Order Ref: 6787A

Distributed by:
International Music Publications Limited
Griffin House, 161 Hammersmith Road, London W6 8BS

International Music Publications Germany
Marstallstrasse 8, D-80539 München, Germany

Danmusik
Vognmagergade 7, DK1120 Copenhagen K, Denmark

Nouva Carisch Srl.
Via Campania 12, 20098 San Giuliano Milanese, Milano, Italy

Carisch Musicom
25 rue d'Hauteville, 75010 Paris, France

Nueva Carisch España
Magallenes 25, 28015 Madrid, Spain

Warner Bros Publications Inc, USA
145800 NW 48th Avenue, PO Box 4340, Miami, Florida 33014, USA

Warner/Chappell Music Inc, Australia
1 Cassius Avenue, North Sydney, New South Wales 2060, Australia

Warner/Chappell Notservice AB
PO Box 533, Vendevägen 85 B, S-182 15 Danderyd, Sweden

Music transcribed and processed by
Barnes Music Engraving Limited
East Sussex TN22 4HA

Cover design by xheight design limited

Printed by Nuova Carisch, Milano, Italy

the **BIOGRAPHY**

BIOGRAPHY

As the history of popular music develops, one fact shines through: talent wins. You can't cheat and survive for any length of time. You can't hype and fool people more than once. You can't hide behind image makers, or alluring videos, or the cut of this season's clothes. Or you can – but then you die. To survive you must evolve, improve, have faith, still thrill. Longevity depends on making the best music.

George Michael has never thought of popular music as a career: it's far more personal – more precious – than that. But he has always taken the long-term view, that ultimately an artist's achievement will not be judged in terms of number one singles, or magazine covers, or prestigious awards, but by a large body of work, a collection of albums over time, a lifetime's development in an artform that no longer depends on shock or rebellion or the quick burn-out to make a mark.

In 16 years, and at 35 years of age, George Michael can already look back on more than 65 million record sales worldwide. He's notched up six US No.1 singles from his debut album, eleven British No.1 singles and six No.1 albums to date. He has also played at some of the biggest and most important concerts in history (Live Aid, the Nelson Mandela Freedom Concert, the Freddie Mercury Tribute), all in front of capacity audiences at Wembley Stadium and in front of many millions watching throughout the world. But that was the beginning, an early phase or two. George Michael was born Georgios Kyriacos Panayiotou on 25th June 1963 in North London, and went on to meet his future Wham! partner Andrew Ridgeley at a nearby comprehensive school. They formed their first band, The Executive, in 1981, but soon realised their chosen path lay as a duo: Wham! was born. Within a year they had released their classic debut single, *Wham Rap*, but it was their second single *Young Guns (Go For It!)* which became the first in a string of Top Ten hits.

In the summer of 1984 George unveiled a glimpse of what was to come by releasing the classic *Careless Whisper*. His first solo single while still with Wham! became one of the signatures of the Eighties and one of the most played radio songs of the decade. It was written when he was still only 17.

His growing maturity was further established with the release of *A Different Corner*, his second solo single, and another mature ballad of lasting worth. A few months later George and Andrew decided that Wham! should disband while still at the very peak of their success. This announcement was followed by a unique final concert at Wembley, an emotional farewell in front of an audience of 72,000. Their place was assured as one of the most exuberant pop bands of the Eighties. Equally certain was that George was set for a remarkable solo career.

In 1987 George became the first white male vocalist ever to duet with soul great Aretha Franklin. The resulting recording *I Knew You Were Waiting*, shot straight to the top of the charts worldwide, starting off a year which saw George jetting between London and Denmark, recording tracks for his outstanding debut album **Faith**.

The album, released in November 1987, showed George Michael to be one of the finest songwriters of the decade and guaranteed him a whole new audience. The album was a No.1 on both sides of the Atlantic, with worldwide sales approaching 15 million.

Faith received a Grammy for the Best Album of 1988, and won George two Ivor Novello Awards for Songwriter Of The Year and International Hit Of The Year (*Faith*). George also won American Music Awards for Favourite Male Vocalist (pop/rock), Favourite Male Artist (soul/R&B) and Favourite Album (soul/R&B).

In America, the outstanding success of **Faith** was marked by six No.1 singles: *I Want Your Sex*, *Faith*, *Father Figure*, *One More Try*, *Monkey* and *Kissing A Fool*.

The live **Faith** tour followed in February 1988, taking the hits package to a momentous opening date at Tokyo's Budokhan Stadium, and then on to ecstatic audiences in Australia, Europe and North America. In June, George interrupted the tour to sing three songs at Wembley Stadium's Nelson Mandela Freedom Concert.

By September 1990 George had gathered together a new body of work – **Listen Without Prejudice: Vol.1** – and another new direction was visible from the first single, *Praying For Time*. Much of the album had a raw, stripped-down feel, and drew heavily from classic Sixties tracks, black rhythm and jazz moods. Mostly they were personal, increasingly philosophical songs; once again they went against the prevailing chart trends.

His videos created new waves too: it was almost unheard of for an artist of his stature not to appear centre-stage, but for *Freedom '90* he found other stars – Cindy Crawford, Naomi Campbell, Christy Turlington and Linda Evangelista. This was the first time these supermodels had been seen together away from the catwalks, and it was an attraction no one found able to resist thereafter.

The album was another British No.1, and also spawned the hit singles *Waiting For That Day*, *Heal The Pain* and *Cowboys and Angels*. Still in his twenties, Michael was already being classed alongside those artists he admired most, and with whom he had the honour of dueting: Aretha Franklin, Elton John and Stevie Wonder. He brought out an autobiography to coincide with the new album ('Bare', co-written with Tony Parsons), and was granted a UK television special, an ultimate cultural sign of arrival.

In November 1991 George released *Don't Let The Sun Go Down On Me*, a duet with Elton John from one of George's Wembley concerts. The song was another No.1 worldwide, and all proceeds went to the AIDS hospice London Lighthouse and the Rainbow Trust Children's Charity.

A few months later George was in the charts once more with *Too Funky*, a single from the **Red Hot and Dance** AIDS charity album, which included a collection of remixed hits by artists such as Madonna and Seal as well as three brand new George Michael songs – the only new songs on the album.

Too Funky went on to become Europe's most played record of 1992, helped partly by the video directed by George and styled by designer Thierry Mugler.

In early 1993 George spent three weeks at the top of the charts with **Five Live EP**, featuring duets with Queen and Lisa Stansfield on tracks from the 1992 Freddie Mercury Tribute Concert and from his own **Cover To Cover** tour in 1991. All proceeds went to the Freddie Mercury Phoenix Trust.

In October of the same year, in a bold statement, making headlines worldwide, George appeared in court against his record company Sony Music Entertainment, as he attempted to break free from the company he claimed no longer accepted his musical direction. Nine months later, the judge found in favour of the record company. An appeal was issued, and was due to be heard in 1996.

On 1st December 1993, World AIDS Day, George played a benefit concert in front of the late Diana, Princess of Wales. This 'Concert Of Hope' also featured kd lang and Mick Hucknall and was televised worldwide, doing much to raise funds and awareness of the disease.

Towards the end of 1994 Michael performed a new song on the first MTV European Music Awards, in the shadow of the Brandenburg Gate in Berlin. *Jesus To A Child* was the first new George Michael song the huge television audience had heard for almost three years, and the acclaim was universal.

Undeterred by the fact that he still wasn't able to release any new material, *Careless Whisper* was voted Londoner's favourite record of all time in January 1995 in a competition run jointly by the capital's leading evening newspaper and radio station. He was then voted Best Male Singer by the same radio station, and by the readers of a national newspaper. In April 1996, George won the Capital Radio award for the 'Best Male Singer' once more and was also honoured with an 'Outstanding Contribution To Music' award.

By July 1995, after many months of negotiations, it was agreed that Michael would leave Sony and sign two new deals, one with Virgin Records for the World excluding the United States and the other with Steven Spielberg, David Geffen and Jeffrey Katzenberg's newly formed SKG Music in North America.

George's first album for Virgin Records, **Older**, was released on 13 May 1996 and thus far the global sales have been outstanding. The album has already earned multi-platinum and/or gold status in 34 countries, including 5 x platinum in the UK.

Written, arranged and produced by George Michael, **Older** was recorded in

London and features 11 brand new tracks including the huge international hits, *Jesus To A Child*, *Fastlove* and *Spinning The Wheel*, the double A-side *Older/I Can't Make You Love Me* and *Star People '97*.

The video for *Fastlove* was also the top choice of MTV Europe viewers in September 1996, as it picked up the 'MTV Europe International Viewers Choice Award' at the MTV Video Music Awards in New York.

At the beginning of October 1996, George performed his first live shows for five years, with a gig for Radio 1FM followed by an Unplugged Session for MTV. Although these concerts were attended by the smallest number of audiences George has ever played to, he claims they were nevertheless two of the most enjoyable, due to the intimacy of the occasion. The Radio 1FM audience consisted of just 200 people and the MTV Unplugged session slightly larger at 500. Both audiences included competition winners, some of whom had flown to London from all over the world, as well as various specially invited guests. At both of these events, George performed a stunning set which included the tracks *Father Figure*, *One More Try*, *Waiting For That Day*, *Freedom*, *Fastlove* and *Older*, closing with the uptempo *Star People* which had the audience up on their feet begging for more.

George has recently been voted 'Best British Male', at the MTV, and the BRITs, and at The Ivor Novello Awards, he was awarded the prestigious title of 'Songwriter of The Year' for the third time.

Adding further distinction to what had already been a fantastic year, George has launched his own record label 'Aegean', a project which is very close to his heart and to which he is completely committed. The label's first single, *Waltz Away Dreaming*, a moving duet by first signing Toby Bourke and George, was released on 26th May, and went straight into the UK Top 10.

On 8th September, George released a 4 track E.P. entitled **You Have Been Loved** which debuted at number 2 making him the first artist in chart history to have 6 top 3 singles from one album.

On 24th November 1997, his former record label Epic released **If You Were There** – the long awaited collection of Wham's Greatest Hits and on 1st December, Virgin Records released a limited edition of George's **Older** album which contains a bonus disc of 6 remixed tracks entitled **Upper**. The **Upper** CD is very exclusive in the fact that it includes interactive elements, allowing fans access to George's web site, videos and fan club through the internet.

In 1998 **Ladies and Gentlemen: The Best of George Michael** was released on Epic Records as agreed in the Sony settlement of 1995. The album soared to the top of the charts in the week of its release, 9th November, and remained at Number 1 for eight weeks, selling over 2 million copies, during the notoriously competitive Christmas period. The album features songs from every era of Michael's career from *Careless Whisper* to the three brilliant brand new tracks. *Outside* was released on 19th October 1998 with an accompanying video that had George Michael's contraversial stamp very clearly on it.

The end of 1998 brought George Michael more accolades. **Ladies and Gentlemen...** achieved six platinum awards in the UK and reached number one on the combined European Album Chart. Michael also topped the polls of the 95.8 Capital FM Hall of Fame for a record eighth time. On 5th December 1998 a one hour Parkinson special was screened on BBC1 to universal critical and public acclaim.

In March 1999 George Michael released *As*, a duet with R&B Diva Mary J Blige, written and originally released by Stevie Wonder on his **Songs in the Key Of Life** album. It was another hit.

the DISCOGRAPHY

DISCOGRAPHY 1984-1999

Careless Whisper (Michael)/**Careless Whisper** (instrumental) (Michael)
Epic A 4603
Released: August 1984

A Different Corner (Michael)/**A Different Corner** (instrumental) (Michael)
Epic A 7033
Released: March 1986

I Knew You Were Waiting (For Me) (Morgan, Climie)/**I Knew You Were Waiting (For Me)** (instrumental) (Morgan, Climie)
Epic DUET 2
Released: January 1987

I Want Your Sex (Monogamy Mix: Rhythm 1 Lust, Rhythm 2 Brass In Love, Rhythm 3 A Last Request) (Michael)
Epic CDLUST 1
Released: June 1987

Faith (Michael)/**Hand To Mouth** (Michael)
Epic EMU 3
Released: October 1987

Faith
Epic CD 460000 9
Released: November 1987
Titles: Faith (Michael)/Father Figure(Michael)/I Want Your Sex(Michael)/One More Try(Michael)/Hard Day(Michael)/Hand To Mouth(Michael)/Look At Your Hands (Michael, Austin)/Monkey(Michael)/Kissing A Fool(Michael)/Hard Day (remix) (Michael)/I Want Your Sex (Part III 'A Last Request') (Michael)

Father Figure (Michael)/**Love's In Need Of Love Today** (Wonder)/**Father Figure** (instrumental) (Michael)
Epic CDEMU 4
Released: January 1988

One More Try (Michael)/**Look At Your Hands** (Michael, Austin)
Epic CDEMU 5
Released: April 1988

Monkey (Michael)/**Monkey** (A'Capella) (Michael)
Epic EMU 6
Released: June 1988

Kissing A Fool (Michael)/**Kissing A Fool** (instrumental) (Michael)/**A Last Request (I Want Your Sex Part 3)** (Michael)
Epic CDEMU 7
Released: November 1988

I Want Your Sex (Parts 1 & 2) (Michael)/**A Different Corner** (Michael)/**Careless Whisper** (Michael)
Epic Solid Gold 654 601-3
Released: May 1989

Praying For Time (Michael)/**If You Were My Woman** (McMurray, Sawyer, Ware)
Epic CDGEO 1
Released: August 1990

Listen Without Prejudice Volume 1
Epic 467295 2
Released: September 1990
Titles: Praying For Time (Michael)/Freedom '90 (Michael)/They Won't Go When I Go (Wonder, Wright)/Something To Save (Michael)/Cowboys And Angels (Michael)/Waiting For That Day (Michael)/Mother's Pride (Michael)/Heal The Pain (Michael)/Soul Free (Michael)/Waiting (Michael)

Waiting For That Day (Michael)/**Fantasy** (Michael)/**Father Figure** (Michael)/**Kissing A Fool** (Michael)
Epic CDGEO 2
Released: October 1990

Freedom '90 (Michael)/**Mother's Pride** (Michael)/**Freedom** (Back To Reality Mix) (Michael)
Epic GEO C3
Released: December 1990

Heal The Pain (Michael)/**Soul Free** (Michael)/**Hand To Mouth** (Michael)
Epic 656 647 5
Released: February 1991

Cowboys And Angels (Michael)/**Something To Save** (Michael)
Epic 6567742
Released: March 1991

Don't Let The Sun Go Down On Me (John, Taupin)/**I Believe (When I Fall In Love It Will Be Forever)** (Wonder, Wright)/**If You Were My Woman** (McMurray, Sawyer, Ware)/**Fantasy** (Michael)
Epic 657 646 2
Released: November 1991

Too Funky (Michael)/**Crazy Man Dance** (Michael)/**Too Funky** (extended) (Michael)
Epic 658 058 2
Released: June 1992

Five Live EP: Somebody To Love (Mercury)/**Killer/Papa Was A Rolling Stone**
(Samuel, Tinley, Whitfield, Strong)/**These Are The Days Of Our Lives** (Queen)/**Calling You** (Telson)
Parlophone CDRS 6340
Released: April 1993

Jesus To A Child (Michael)/**One More Try** (live gospel version) (Michael)/**Older** (instrumental version) (Michael)
Virgin VSCDG 1571
Released: January 1996

Fastlove (Part 1) (Michael)/**I'm Your Man** (Michael)/**Fastlove** (Part II fully extended mix)
Virgin VSCDG 1579
Released: April 1996

Older

Virgin CDV 2802
Released: May 1996
Titles: Like Jesus To A Child (Michael)/Fastlove (Michael)/Older (Michael)/Spinning The Wheel (Michael, Douglas)/It Doesn't Really Matter (Michael)/The Strangest Thing (Michael)/To Be Forgiven (Michael)/Move On (Michael)/Star People (Michael)/You Have Been Loved (Michael, Austin)/Free (Michael)

Spinning The Wheel EP: Spinning The Wheel (Michael, Douglas)/**You Know That I Want To** (Michael, Douglas)/**Safe** (Michael)/**Spinning The Wheel** (forthright edit) (Michael, Douglas)
Virgin VSCDG 1595
Released: August 1996

Older EP: Older (radio edit) (Michael)/**I Can't Make You Love Me** (Reid, Shamblin)/ **Desafinado** (with Astrud Gilberto) (Mendonca, Jobim)/**The Strangest Thing** (live) (Michael)
Virgin VSCDG 1626
Released: January 1997

Star People '97 (Michael)/**Everything She Wants** (Michael)/**Star People** (Unplugged) (Michael)
Virgin VSCDG 1641
Released: April 1997

Waltz Away Dreaming (Michael, Bourke)/**Things I Said Tonight** (Bourke)
Ægean AECD 01
Released: May 1997

You Have Been Loved EP: You Have Been Loved (Michael)/**The Strangest Thing '97** (radio mix) (Michael)/**Father Figure** (Unplugged) (Michael)/**Praying For Time** (Unplugged)
Virgin VSCDG 1663
Released: September 1997

Ladies And Gentlemen: The Best Of George Michael
Epic 491 705 2
Released: October 1998
Titles: CD 1 From The Heart: Jesus To A Child (Michael)/Father Figure (Michael)/Careless Whisper (Michael, Ridgeley)/Don't Let The Sun Go Down On Me (John, Taupin)/You Have Been Loved (Michael, Austin)/Kissing A Fool (Michael)/I Can't Make You Love Me (Reid, Shamblin)/Heal The Pain (Michael)/Moment With You (Michael)/Desafinado (Mendonca, Jobim) Cowboys And Angels (Michael)/Praying For Time (Michael)/One More Try (Michael)/A Different Corner (Michael)
CD 2 For The Feet: Outside (Michael)/As (Wonder)/Fastlove (Michael)/Too Funky (Michael)/Freedom '90 (Michael)/Star People '97 (Michael)/Killer/Papa Was A Rolling Stone (Samuel, Tinley, Whitfield, Strong)/I Want Your Sex (Michael)/The Strangest Thing (Michael)/Fantasy (Michael)/Spinning The Wheel (Michael, Douglas)/Waiting For That Day (Michael)/I Knew You Were Waiting (For Me) (Morgan, Climie)/Faith (Michael)/Somebody To Love (Mercury)

As (Wonder)
Epic 6670125
Released: July 1999

Songs From The Last Century
Virgin CDVX 2920
Released: December 1999
Titles: Brother, Can You Spare A Dime? (Gorney, Harburg)/Roxanne (Sumner)/You've Changed (Fischer, Carey)/My Baby Just Cares For Me (Donaldson, Kahn)/The First Time Ever I Saw Your Face (McColl)/Miss Sarajevo (Eno, Hewton, Clayton, Evans, ...)/I Remember You (Schertzinger, Mercer)/Secret Love (Fain, Webster)/Wild Is The Wind (Tiomkin, Washington)/Where Or When/It's Alright With Me (Rodgers, Hart, Porter)

the LYRICS

1   As _____

George Michael
As around the sun the earth knows she's revolving
And the rosebuds know to bloom in early May
Just as hate knows love's the cure
You can rest your mind assured
That I'll be loving you always

As now can't reveal the mystery of tomorrow
But in passing will grow older every day
Just as all that's born is new
You know what I say is true
That I'll be loving you always

(Until the rainbow burns the stars out of the sky)
Always
(Until the ocean covers every mountain high)
Always
(Until the day that eight times eight
         times eight is four)
Always
(Until the day that is the day that are no more)

Mary Jo Blige
Did you know that true love asks for nothing
Her acceptance is the way we pay
Did you know that life has given love a guarantee
To last through forever another day

G.M.
As today I know I'm living
         but tomorrow could make the past
But that I mustn't fear 'cause you're here
M.J.B.
Now I know deep in my mind
         the love of me I've left behind
G.M.
And I'll be loving you always

Chorus
Until the rainbow burns the stars out of the sky
Until the ocean covers every mountain high
Until the dolphin flies and parrots live at sea
Until we dream of life and life becomes a dream

Until the day is night and night becomes the day
Until the trees and seas just up and fly away
Until the day that eight times eight times is four
Until the day that is the day that are no more

G.M.
Did you know that true love asks for nothing
Her acceptance is the way we pay
Did you know that life has given love a guarantee
To last through forever
M.J.B.
Another day

G.M.
As around the sun the earth knows she's revolving
And the rosebuds know to bloom in early May
M.J.B.
Now I know deep in my mind the love of me I've left
         behind
G.M.
And I'll be loving you always

Repeat Chorus to fade

Words and Music by Stevie Wonder

© 1975 & 2000 Black Bull Music Inc/
Jobete Music Co Inc, London WC2H 0EA

2   Brother Can You Spare A Dime? __

Once I built a railroad, made it run
Made it race against time
Once I built a railroad, now it's done
Brother can you spare a dime?

Once I built a tower to the sun
Brick and rivet and lime
Once I built a tower, now it's done
Brother can you spare a dime?

Once in khaki suits, gee we looked swell
Full of that Yankee Doodle de dum
Half a million boots went slogging through hell
I was the kid with the drum

Say don't you remember they called me Al
It was Al all the time
Say don't you remember I'm your pal
Brother can you spare a dime?
Buddy can you spare a dime?

Words by E Y Harburg
Music by Jay Gorney

© 1932 Harms Inc, USA
Warner/Chappell Music Ltd, London W6 8BS

3 Calling You

A desert road from Vegas to nowhere
Some place better than where you've been
A coffee machine that needs some fixing
In a little café just around the bend

I am calling you
Well can't you hear me?
I am calling you

I am calling you
Can't you hear me?
I am calling you

A desert road from Vegas to nowhere
Some place better than where you've been
A coffee machine that needs some fixing
In a little café just around the bend

A hot, dry wind blows right through me
The baby's crying so I can't sleep
We both know a change is coming
Coming closer to sweet release

I am calling you
Can't you hear me?
I am calling you

A desert road from Vegas to nowhere

Words and Music by Robert Eria Telson

© 1993 & 2000 Boodle Music, USA
BMG Music Publishing Ltd, London SW6 3JW

4 Careless Whisper

I feel so unsure
As I take your hand
And lead you to the dance floor
As the music dies
Something in your eyes
Calls to mind a silver screen
And you're its sad goodbye

I'm never gonna dance again
Guilty feet have got no rhythm
Though it's easy to pretend
I know you're not a fool
I should have known better
Than to cheat a friend
And waste the chance that I've been given
So I'm never gonna dance again
The way I dance with you

Time can never mend
The careless whispers
Of a good friend
To the heart and mind
Ignorance is kind
There's no comfort in the truth
Pain is the heart you'll find

I'm never gonna dance again
Guilty feet have got no rhythm
Though its easy to pretend
I know you're not a fool

I should have known better
Than to cheat a friend
And waste the chance that I've been given
So I'm never gonna dance again
The way I dance with you

Tonight the music seems so loud
I wish that we could lose this crowd
Maybe its better this way
We'd hurt each other with the things we want to say
We could have been so good together
We could have lived this dance forever
But now who's gonna dance with me
Please stay

I'm never gonna dance again
Guilty feet have got no rhythm
Though it's easy to pretend
I know you're not a fool
Should have known better
Than to cheat a friend
And waste a chance that I've been given
So I'm never gonna dance again
The way I dance with you

Now that you're gone
Was what I did so wrong, so wrong
That you had to leave me all alone

Words and Music by George Michael and Andrew Ridgeley

© 1984 & 2000 Morrison Leahy Music Ltd, London W2 1QD

5   Cowboys And Angels _____

When your heart's in someone else's hands
Monkey see and monkey do
Their wish is your command
You're not to blame
Everyone's the same

All you do is love
And love is all you do
I should know by now
The way I fought for you
You're not to blame
Everyone's the same

I know you think
That you're safe mister
Harmless deception that keeps love at bay
It's the ones who resist
That we most want to kiss
Wouldn't you say

Cowboys and angels
They have all the time for you
Why should I imagine
That I'd be a find for you
Why should I imagine
That I'd have something to say

But that scar on your face
That beautiful face of yours
In your heart there's a trace
Of someone before

When your heart's in someone else's plans
Things you say and things you do
They don't understand
It's such a shame
Always ends the same

You can call it love
But I don't think it's true
You should know by now
I'm not the boy for you
You're not to blame
Always ends the same

I know you think
That you're safe sister
Harmless affection
That keeps things this way
It's the ones who persist
For the sake of a kiss
Who will pay

Cowboys and angels
They all take a shine to you
Why should I imagine
That I was designed for you
Why should I believe
That you would stay

But that scar on your face
That beautiful face of yours
Don't you think that I know
They've hurt you before

Take this man to your bed
Maybe his hands
Will help you forget
Please be stronger than your past
The future may still give you a chance

Words and Music by George Michael

6 Crazyman Dance ⎯⎯⎯⎯⎯⎯

Well I'm still here
But I'm so scared
I've got myself in trouble
So much trouble
I know I'm gonna make it
But I just can't take New York
I just can't take New York

My middle name is fear
I have a vacant stare
And it's been so long
Since my body's been warm
I know I've gotta make it
But I just can't take New York
I just can't take New York

I came here all dreams and wide eyes
In the big, big city
No family, no money
And I don't even know what's hit me
(New York)

Every step and every corner
Watch them drowning
Watch them do the Crazyman Dance
Watch them do the Crazyman Dance

Men and women to the slaughter
We just stand and watch them do
        the Crazyman Dance
Watch them do the Crazyman Dance

It's been one whole year
And it's just not fair
For all the pushing and shoving
I've still got nothing
I'm never gonna make it
And I'm stuck here in New York
I'm stuck here in New York

So people don't come near
Unless you've got a dollar to spare
'Cause you know what they say
About madmen on the subways of New York
(Believe it)

Yesterday's newspapers
I wrap them around my body
Outside these skyscrapers
I wait for the night to hit me
And boy does it hit me

Just like your ma, just like your pa
Just like someone you used to know

Every street and every corner
Watch them drowning
Watch them do the Crazyman Dance
For a nickel or a quarter
For your pleasure
Watch them do the Crazyman Dance

I'm coming to London
I'm coming to Paris
I'm gonna make
You good clean people embarrassed
Why don't you look at my face
Why don't you look in my eyes
You'd rather look at your feet
You'd rather look at the skies
Oh you'd look anywhere
But at a man whose pure existance
Says 'I ain't got time'
And I don't care, I don't care
You just don't care

Words and Music by George Michael

© 1992 & 2000 Morrison Leahy Music Ltd, London W2 1QD

7 Desafinado

George Michael
Se você disser que eu desafino amor
Saiba que isto em mim provocaimensa dôr
Só privilegia dos têm ou vidoigual ao seu
Eu possuo a penas o que deus me deu

Astrud Gilberto
Se você insiste em classificar
O meu comportamento de anti musical
Eu mesmo mentindo possoargumentar
Both
Que is to é bossa nova
Que is to é mui to natural

A.G.
O que você nao sabe nem siquer presente
É que os desafinados tambem têm coracoa

G.M.
Fotografei vocé na minha rolleiflex
Revelouse a sua enor mein gratidão

G.M.
Só nao podera falar assim do meu amor
A.G.
É le é o maior
Both
Que você pode encontrar
Você com a sua musica es que ceu o principal
Que no peito dos desafinados
No fundo do peito bate cala do
No peito dos desafinados tambem bate um coracoa

Words by Newton Ferriera de Mendonca
Music by Antonio Carlos Jobim

8 A Different Corner

I'd say love was a magical thing
I'd say love would keep us from pain
Had I been there, had I been there

I would promise you all of my life
But to lose you would cut like a knife
So I don't dare, no I don't dare

'Cause I've never come close
In all of these years
You are the only one to stop my tears
And I'm scared, I'm so scared

Take me back in time
Maybe I can forget
Turn a different corner
And we never would have met
Would you care?

I don't understand it
For you it's a breeze
Little by little
You've brought me to my knees
Don't you care?

No I've never come close
In all of these years
You are the only one to stop my tears
I'm so scared of this love

And if all that there is
Is this fear of being used
I should go back to being lonely and confused
If I could, I would, I swear

Words and Music by George Michael

9   Do You Really Want To Know ──

When I ask those questions baby
It's just to get them out of my head
'Cause they turn around inside it
And they spill on to our bed

But do I really want to know?
Do I really want to know your life?
Would I have to let you go
Could I listen to my heart
If my head stopped to think twice

Well I've been a good boy
And I've been a bad boy
I have too much fun
But baby so did everyone
I've never been an angel
But things are gonna change

So do you really want to know?
Do you really want to know my life?
Would you have to let me go?
Could you listen to your heart
If your head stopped to think twice?

If you knew every woman
And I knew every man
We never would have made it past holding hands
I guess the saying is no longer true
That what you don't know can't hurt you

I guess there's just no question baby
You know what you're doing in bed
If I want your touch
Should I know too much
Some things are better left unsaid

So do I really want to know?
Do I really want to know your life?
Would I have to let you go?
Could I listen to my heart
If my head stopped to think twice?

(Tell me baby
It's one thing to guess
It's one thing to know
And don't you think that maybe baby
I've got secrets of my own?)

If I knew every woman
And you knew every man
We never would have made it past holding hands
I used to say it but it's no longer true
'Cause what you don't know can really hurt you
(It can kill you baby)

Even as we speak
The world is full of lovers
Night after night, week after week
Trusting to luck and a pocket full of rubbers

Words and Music by George Michael

© 1992 & 2000 Dick Leahy Music Ltd, London W2 1QD

10   Don't Let The Sun Go Down On Me

I can't light no more of your darkness
All my pictures seem to fade to black and white
I'm growing tired and time stands still before me
Frozen here on the ladder of my life

It's much too late to save myself from falling
I took a chance and changed your way of life
But you misread my meaning when I met you
Closed the door and left me blinded by the light

Don't let the sun go down on me
Although I search myself
            it's always someone else I see
I'd just allow a fragment of your life to wander free
But losing everything
            is like the sun going down on me

I can't find oh the right romantic line
But see me once and see the way I feel
Don't discard me
            just because you think I mean you harm
But these cuts I have
            oh they need love to help them heal

Don't let the sun go down on me
Although I search myself
            it's always someone else I see
I'd just allow a fragment of your life to wonder free
'Cause losing everything
            is like the sun going down on me

Words and Music by Elton John and Bernie Taupin

© 1974 & 2000 Big Pig Music Ltd, London W6 8BS

11 Everything She Wants

Somebody told me
Boy everything she wants is everything she sees
I guess I must have loved you
Because I said you were the pefect girl for me baby

And now we're six months older
And everything you want and everything you see
Is out of reach, not good enough
I don't know what the hell you want from me

Somebody tell me
(Won't you tell me)
Why I work so hard for you
(To give you money, work to give you money)

Some people work for a living
Some people for fun, girl I just work for you
They told me marriage was give and take
Well you've shown me you can take
You've got some giving to do

And now you tell me that you're having my baby
I'll tell you that I'm happy if you want me to
But one step further and my back will break
If my best isn't good enough
Then how can it be good enough for two
I can't even work any harder than I do

Somebody tell me
(Won't you tell me)
Why I work so hard for you
(To give you money, work to give you money)

Why do I do the things I do
I'd tell you if I knew
My God I don't even think that I love you
Won't you tell me
Give you money
Work to give you money

Words and Music by George Michael

© 1984 & 2000 Morrison Leahy Music Ltd, London W2 1QD

12 Faith

Well I guess it would be nice
If I could touch your body
I know not everybody
Has got a body like you
But I've got to think twice
Before I give my heart away
And I know all the games you play
Because I played them too

But I need some time off from that emotion
Time to pick my heart up off the floor
When that love comes down without devotion
Well it takes a strong man baby
But I'm showing you the door

Because I've got to have faith
I've got to have faith
Because I've got to have faith, faith, faith
I've got to have faith, a-faith, -faith

Baby I know you're asking me to stay
Stay please, please, please don't go away
You say I'm giving you the blues
Maybe you mean every word you say
Can't help but think of yesterday
And another who tied me down to lover boy rules

Before this river becomes an ocean
Before you throw my heart back on the floor
Oh baby I reconsider my foolish notion
Well I need someone to hold me
But I'll wait for something more

Yes I've got to have faith
I've got to have faith
Because I've got to have faith, faith, faith
I've got to have faith, a-faith, -faith

Words and Music by George Michael

© 1987 & 2000 Morrison Leahy Music Ltd, London W2 1QD

13 Fastlove _____

Gotta get up to get down
You gotta get up to get
Gotta get up to get down
You gotta get up to get down

Looking for some education
Made my way into the night
All that bullshit conversation
Baby can't you read the signs

I won't bore you with the detail baby
I don't even want to waste your time
Let's just say that maybe
You could help to ease my mind

Baby I ain't Mister Right
But if you're looking for fast love
If that's love in your eyes
It's more than enough
Had some bad love
So fast love is all
That I've got on my mind

Looking for some affirmation
Made my way into the sun
My friends got their ladies
They're all having babies
But I just want to have some fun

I won't bore you with the detail baby
Gotta get there in your own sweet time
Lets just say that maybe
You could help me ease my mind

Baby I ain't Mister Right
But if you're looking for fast love
If that's love in your eyes
It's more than enough
Had some bad love
So fast love is all
That I've got on my mind

Gotta get up to get down
Gotta get up to get down

In the absence of security
I made my way into the night
Stupid Cupid keeps on calling me
But I see nothing in his eyes

I miss my baby
I miss my baby tonight
So why don't we make a little room
In my B.M.W. babe
Searching for some peace of mind
I'll help you find it
I do believe that we are
Practicing the same religion
Oh you really ought to get up now

That's right
Oh you really ought to get up
Gotta get up to get down
You gotta get up to get down

Words and Music by George Michael

14 Fantasy

One day you say you love
The next you tell me you don't
One day you say you will
And the next you tell me you won't
Hey little baby
There ain't much point me hanging around

One day you make me feel that your love
Is in my hands
One day you say you'll stay
And the next
You're changing your plans
Hey little baby
Ain't much point in hanging around
'Cause if you ain't got time for me
I'll find another fantasy

It's kind of funny that you think
That I'm the boy to make you cry
I could make you happy
If only for a while
Little baby, little baby
I can give you all the loving
That your heart desires
If you ain't got time for me
I'll find another fantasy

I said it could be the price of love
Could be the price of hate
What am I guilty of
Why do you make me wait so long
I don't know your intentions
Look to the skies above
I'm in the hands of fate
Push till I get to shove

I've got to know for heaven's sake
Is this love or invention
Baby can't you see
I'll find another fantasy

You hang around with people
Who are sure to make you cry
I can make you happy
If only for a while
Little baby, little baby
I can give you all the loving
That your heart desires
If only for a while
Little baby, little baby
I can give you all the loving
That your heart desires
'Cause if you ain't got time for me
I'll find another fantasy

You take someone's heart
And you kick it around
Keep on picking it up
So you can watch it come down
I don't know what I'm supposed to do
While I wait for you to make up your mind
Could you please be so kind
When you know what to do
I'll be in the next room
But if you leave it too late
I may be in the next state

Words and Music by George Michael

15 Father Figure _____

That's all I wanted
Something special
Something sacred
In your eyes
For just one moment
To be bold and naked
At your side
Sometimes I think that
You never understand me
Maybe this time is forever
Say it can be

That's all you wanted
Something special
Someone sacred
In your life
Just for one moment
To be warm and naked
At my side
Sometimes I think that
You'll never understand me
But something tells me
Together we'd be happy

I will be your father figure
Put your tiny hand in mine
I will be your preacher teacher
Anything you have in mind
I will be your father figure
I have had enough of crime
I will be the one who loves you
Till the end of time

That's all I wanted
But sometimes love
Can be mistaken
For a crime
That's all I wanted
Just to see my baby's
Blue eyes shine

This time I think that
My lover understands me
If we have faith in each other
Then we can be strong baby

I will be your father figure
Put your tiny hand in mine
I will be your preacher teacher
Anything you have in mind
I will be your father figure
I have had enough of crime
I will be the one who loves you
Till the end of time

If you were the desert
I'll be the sea
If you ever hunger
Hunger for me
Whatever you asked for
That's what I'll be

So when you remember
The ones who have lied
Who said that they cared
But then laughed as you cried
Beautiful darling
Don't think of me
Because all I ever wanted
Is in your eyes baby
And love can't lie

Greet me with the eyes of a child
My love is always telling me so
Heaven is a kiss and a smile
Just hold on, hold on
Won't let you go my baby

I will be your father figure
Put your tiny hand in mine
I will be your preacher teacher
Anything you have in mind
I will be your father figure
I have had enough of crime
So I am gonna love you
Till the end of time

Words and Music by George Michael

16   The First Time Ever I Saw Your Face

The first time ever I saw your face
I thought the sun rose in your eyes
The moon and the stars were the gifts you gave
To the dark and endless skies my love
To the dark and empty skies

And the first time ever I kissed your mouth
I felt the earth move in my hands
Like the trembling heart of a captive bird
That was there at my command my love
That was there

And the first time ever I lay with you
And felt your heart so close to mine
And I knew our joy would fill the earth
And would last till the end of time my love
It would last till the end of time

The first time ever I saw your face
Your face, your face

Words and Music by Ewan McColl

© 1962 Stormking Music Inc, USA
© 1972 Harmony Music Ltd, London W8 7TQ

17   Free

Feels good to be free

Words and Music by George Michael

© 1996 & 2000 Dick Leahy Music Ltd, London W2 1QD

18   Freedom

Every day I hear a different story
People saying that you're no good for me
Saw your lover with another
And she's making a fool of you

If you loved me baby, you would deny it
But you laugh and tell me I should try it
Tell me I'm a baby and I don't understand

But you know that I'll forgive you
Just this once, twice, forever
'Cause baby you could drag me to hell and back
Just as long as we're together
And you do

I don't want your freedom
I don't want to play around
I don't want no party baby
Part time love just brings me down
I don't need your freedom
Girl all I want right now is you

Like a prisoner who has his own key
But I can't escape until you love me
I just go from day to day
Knowing all about the other boys
You take my hand and tell me I'm a fool
To give you all that I do
I bet you some day baby
Someone says the same to you

But you know that I'll forgive you
Just this once twice forever
'Cause baby you could drag me to hell and back
Just as long as we're together
And you do

I don't want your freedom
I don't want to play around
I don't want no party baby
Part time love just brings me down
I don't want your freedom
Girl all I want right now is you

You're hurting me baby, hurting me baby
You're hurting me baby, hurting me baby

But you know that I'll forgive you
Just this once twice forever
'Cause baby you could drag me to hell and back
Just as long as we're together
And you do

I don't want your freedom
I don't need to play around
I don't want no party baby
Part time love just brings me down
I don't want your . . .

Words and Music by George Michael

© 1984 & 2000 Morrison Leahy Music Ltd, London W2 1QD

19 Freedom '90

I won't let you down
I will not give you up
Got to have some faith in the sound
It's the one good thing that I've got

I won't let you down
So please don't give me up
'Cause I would really, really love
To stick around

Heaven knows I was just a young boy
Didn't know what I wanted to be
I was every little hungry schoolgirl's pride and joy
And I guess it was enough for me
To win the race, a prettier face
Brand new clothes and a big fat place
On your rock and roll T.V.
But today the way you play the game is not the same
Think I'm gonna get me some happy

I think there's something you should know
I think it's time I told you so
There's something deep inside of me
There's someone else I've got to be
Take back your picture in a frame
Take back your 'Singing In The Rain'
Just hope you'll understand
Sometimes the clothes do not make the man

All we have to do now
Is to take these lies
And make them true somehow
All we have to see
Is that I don't belong to you
And you don't belong to me

(Freedom!)
I won't let you down
(Freedom!)
I will not give you up
(Freedom!)
Got to have some faith in the sound
(You've got to give for what you take)
It's the one good thing that I've got
(Freedom!)
I won't let you down
(Freedom!)
So please don't give me up
(Freedom!)
'Cause I would really, really love to stick around
(You've got to give for what you take)

Heaven knows we sure had some fun boy
What a kick just a buddy and me
We had every big shot good time band on the run
                boy
We were living in a fantasy
We won the race, got outta the place
Went back home, got a brand new face
For the boys at M.T.V.
But today the way I play the game has got to change
Now I'm gonna get me some happy

I think there's something you should know
I think it's time I stopped the show
There's something deep inside of me
There's someone I forgot to be
Take back your picture in the frame
Don't think that I'll be back again
Just hope you'll understand
Sometimes the clothes do not make the man

All we have to do now
Is to take these lies
And make them true somehow
All we have to see
Is that I don't belong to you
And you don't belong to me

(Freedom!)
I won't let you down
(Freedom!)
I will not give you up
(Freedom!)
You've got to live for what you take
Got to have some faith in the sound
It's the one good thing that I've got
(Freedom!)
I won't let you down
(Freedom!)
So please don't give me up
(Freedom!)
'Cause I would really, really love to stick around

Well it looks like the road to heaven
But it feels like the road to hell
But I know which side my bread was buttered
I took the knife as well
Posing for another picture
Everybody's got to sell
But when you shake your ass they notice fast
Some mistakes were built to last

That's what you get
(That's what you get)
That's what you get
(I say that's what you get)
I say that's what you get
For changing your mind
That's what you get
For changing your mind
And after all this time
I just hope you'll understand
Sometimes the clothes do not make the man

Chorus ad lib. to fade

Words and Music by George Michael

20   Hand To Mouth _____

Jimmy got nothing, made himself a name
With a gun that he polished for a rainy day
A smile and a quote from a vigilante movie
Our boy Jimmy just blew them all away
He said it made him crazy
Twenty-five years living hand to mouth
Hand to mouth, hand to mouth

Sweet little baby on a big white doorstep
She needs her mother but her mother is dead
Just another hooker that the lucky can forget
Just another hooker it happens every day
She left a little baby
But she couldn't bear to see him living
Hand to mouth, hand to mouth

I believe in the gods of America
I believe in the land of the Free
And no-one told me
That the gods believe in nothing
So with empty hands I pray
And from day to hopeless day
They still don't see

Everybody talks about the new generation
Jump on the wagon or they'll leave you behind
But no-one gave a thought to the rest of the nation
I'd like to help you buddy, but I haven't got the time
Somebody shouted save me
But everybody started living
Hand to mouth, hand to mouth

There's a big white lady on a big white doorstep
She asked her daddy and her daddy said yes
Has to give a little for the dollars that we get
Has to give a little, they say it's for the best
Somebody shouted maybe
But they kept on living from
Hand to mouth, hand to mouth

So she went to the arms of America
And she kissed the powers that be
And someone told me, someone told me
That the gods believe in nothing
So with empty hands I pray
And I tell myself one day
It just might stop
You just might see

Words and Music by George Michael

21   Happy _____

First you take off your hat
Then you shake off those brand new shoes
'Hey George, what have you got to lose?'
With my hand on your thigh
I just look you in the eye
And say 'Not a whole lot baby
But a whole lot more than you'

I can make you happy
Don't you know that
I can make you happy
I can make you happy
Don't you know that
I can make you happy

Boys and girls
The ones who kiss and tell
Why should we have to believe them?
No I don't understand
How any woman, how any man
Can say 'Lay me down, lay me down'
For that big-stash, cheap-cash
Think-about-the-money

I can make you happy
Don't you know that
I can make you happy

I can make you happy
Don't you know that
I can make you happy

I've seen you in the corner
With your rub-it-on tan
Hitching a ride
Could be a woman or a man
Gonna get what you want before too long
Gonna take your opportunities
Right or wrong
Some poor cow with a seven-year itch?
You don't dig men
But you'll fuck 'em if they're rich
You can't be with me
You're a lowlife daughter
Of a son of a bitch

I can make you happy
Don't you know that
I can make you happy
I can make you happy
Don't you know that
I can make you happy

Words and Music by George Michael

22   Hard Day _____

Don't bring me down
Don't bring me down

I've never been one for playing games
You can move your mouth forever
But the words sound just the same
Something like bang bang, you're dead
Can we just make love instead
Say yes 'cause it's what we do best
I've had such a hard day
Take me where their eyes can't find us
Without you I may as well just . . .

How much do I have to say
What more do you have to see
What will it take to make you love me
Well you're not the first
You're not the last
You're not even the one who loves me the best
But all I think about is you
So take me where their eyes can't find us
Without you I may as well just . . .

Don't bring me down
Don't bring me down

I've never been one for playing games
You can move your mouth forever
But the words sound just the same
Bang bang, you're dead
Shouldn't we just make love instead
Say yes 'cause it's what we do best
I've had such a hard day

Sweet little boy with oh such a big mouth
Harsh words can get you into hot water
When people don't understand you baby
I'm always here for you
And I will never bring you down
Trust me, I want you to trust me
'Cause I won't bring you down
Do you trust me?

Words and Music by George Michael

© 1997 & 2000 Morrison Leahy Music Ltd, London W2 1QD

23   Heal The Pain

Let me tell you a secret
Put it in your heart and keep it
Something that I want you to know
Do something for me
Listen to my simple story
Maybe we'll have something to show
You tell me you're cold on the inside
How can the outside world
Be a place that you heart can embrace?
Be good to yourself
Cause nobody else has the power
To make you happy

How can I help you?
Please let me try to
I can heal the pain
That you're feeling inside
Whenever you want me
You know that I will be
Waiting for the day
That you'll say you'll be mine

He must have really hurt you
To make you say the things that you do
He must have really hurt you
To make those pretty eyes look so blue
He must have known that he could
That you'd never leave him
Now you can't see my love is good
And that I'm not him

How can I help you?
Please let me try to
I can heal the pain
Won't you let me inside
Whenever you want me
You know that I will be
Waiting for the day
That you'll say you'll be mine

Won't you let me
Let this love begin
Won't you show me your heart now
I'll be good to you
I can make this thing true
Show me that heart right now

Who needs a lover that can't be a friend?
Something tells me I'm the one
You've been looking for
If you ever should see him again
Won't you tell him
You've found someone who gives you more
Someone who will protect you
Love and respect you
All those things that he never could
Bring to you like I do
Or rather I would
Won't you show me your heart
Like you should

How can I help you?
Please let me try to
I can heal the pain
That you're feeling inside
Whenever you want me
You know that I will be
Waiting for the day
That you say you'll be mine

Won't you let me in
Let this love begin
Won't you show me your heart now
I'll be good to you
I can make this thing true
And get to your heart somehow

Words and Music by George Michael

24   I Believe (When I Fall In Love) ___

Shattered dreams, worthless years
Here am I encased inside a hollow shell
Life began, then was done
Now I stare into a cold and empty well

Many sounds that greet our ears
The sights our eyes behold
Will open up our merging hearts
And feed our empty souls

I believe when I fall in love with you
It will be forever
I believe when I fall in love this time
It will be forever

Without despair, we will share
And the joys of caring will not be erased
What has been, must never end
The joys of caring will not be replaced

When the seeds of love are planted firm
They won't be hard to find
And the songs of love I sing to you
Will echo in my mind

I believe when I fall in love with you
It will be forever
I believe when I fall in love this time
It will be forever

You know God has answered my prayers
Won't you listen to him now
God for sure will answer my prayers
Won't you listen to him now
God will answer your prayers
Just ask him and God is sure
To answer all your prayers

Oh come on let's fall in love
You're the one that I've been waiting for
Come on let's fall in love
You're the woman that I adore
Don't you wanna fall in love with me baby
Don't you wanna fall in love with me

Words and Music by
Stevie Wonder and Yvonne Wright

25   I Can't Make You Love Me ____

Turn down the lights
Turn down the bed
Turn down these voices
Inside my head
Lay down with me
Tell no lies
Just hold me close
Don't patronize

'Cause I can't make you love me
If you don't
You can't make your heart feel
Something it won't
Here in the dark
In these final hours
I will lay down my heart
And I feel the power
But you won't, no you won't
And I can't make you love me
If you don't

I close my eyes
Then I won't see
The love you do not feel
When you're holding me

Mornin' will come
And I'll do what's right
Just give me till then
To give up this fight
And I will give up this fight

And I can't make you love me
If you don't
You can't make your heart
Feel something that it won't
And here in the dark
In these final hours
I will lay down my heart
I'll feel the power
But you won't, no you won't
And I can't make you love me
If you don't

Ain't no use in you trying
S'no good for me baby without love
All my tears, all these years
Every place I believed in

Someone's gonna love me

Words and Music by Mike Reid and Allen Shamblin

26   I Knew You Were Waiting (For Me)

Aretha Franklin
Like a warrior that fights
And wins the battle
I know the taste of victory
Though I went through some nights
Consumed by the shadows
I was crippled emotionally

George Michael
Somehow I made it through the heartache
Yes I did, I escaped
I found my way out of the darkness
I kept my faith
A.F.
I know you did
G.M.
Kept my faith

Both
When the river was deep
I didn't falter
When the mountain was high
I still believed
When the valley was low
It didn't stop me
I knew you were waiting
Knew you were waiting for me

A.F.
With an endless desire
I kept on searching
Sure in time our eyes would meet
Like the bridge is on fire
The hurt is over
One touch and you set me free

G.M.
No, I don't regret a single moment
No I don't
A.F.
I know you don't
G.M.
Looking back
When I think of all those diappointments
I just laugh
A.F.
I know you do
G.M.
I just laugh

Both
When the river was deep
I didn't falter
When the mountain was high
I still believed
When the valley was low
It didn't stop me
I knew you were waiting
I knew you were waiting for me

So we were drawn together
Through destiny
I know this love we shared
Both
Knew you were waiting
Knew you were waiting
G.M.
I knew you were waiting
Both
Knew you were waiting for me

Words and Music by Dennis Morgan and Simon Climie

© 1986 & 2000 Little Shop Of Morgansongs and
Warner-Tamerlane Pub Corp, USA
Warner/Chappell Music Ltd, London W6 8BS and Chrysalis Music Ltd,
London W10 6SP

27   I Remember You ─────────

I remember you
You're the one who made my dreams come true
A few kisses ago

I remember you
You're the one who said I love you too
Didn't you know?

I remember too
A distant bell and stars that fell
Like rain out of the blue

When my life is through
And the angels ask me to recall
The thrill of them all
Then I will tell them
I remember you

Words and Music by Words by Johnny Mercer
Music by Victor Schertzinger

© 1942 Paramount Music Corporation & Famous Music Corporation

28   I Want Your Sex (Part I 'Lust') ___

There's things that you guess
And things that you know
There's boys you can trust
And girls that you don't
There's little things you hide
And little things that you show
Sometimes you think you're gonna get it
But you don't and that's just the way it goes

I swear I won't tease you
Won't tell you no lies
I don't need no Bible
Just look in my eyes
I've waited so long baby
Now that we're friends
Every man's got his patience
And here's where mine ends

I want your sex, I want your love
I want your sex, I want your sex

It's playing on my mind
It's dancing on my soul
It's taken so much time
So why don't you just let me go
I'd really like to try
I'd really love to know
When you tell me you're gonna regret it
Then I tell you that I love you
But you still say no

I swear I won't tease you
Won't tell you no lies
I don't need no Bible
Just look into my eyes
I've waited so long baby
Out in the cold
But I can't take much more girl
I'm losing control

I want your sex, I want your love
I want your sex, I want your sex

It's natural, it's chemical
It's logical, habitual
It's sensual but most of all
Sex is something we should do
Sex is something for me and you
Sex is natural, sex is good
Not everybody does it
But everybody should
Sex is natural, sex is fun
Sex is best when it's one on one

I'm not your father, I'm not your brother
Talk to your sister, I am a lover
What's your definition of dirty baby?
What do you consider pornography?
Don't you know I love you till it hurts me baby?
Don't you think it's time you had sex with me?

Words and Music by George Michael

© 1987 & 2000 Morrison Leahy Music Ltd, London W2 1QD

29   I Want Your Sex (Part II) _____

Come on
I want you baby

Oh so much love
That you've never seen
Let's make love
Put your trust in me
Don't you listen to what they told you
Because I love you, let me hold you

I'm not your brother
I'm not your father
Oh will you ever change your mind
I'm a gentle lover with a heart of gold
Baby, you've been so unkind

Come on
I want your sex
Come on
I want your sex
That's right, all night
I want your sex
I want your sex

Sexy baby's sexy body
Keeps me guessing with a promise
I know we can come together
But the question is will we ever ever?
Oh together you and me

Words and Music by George Michael

© 1987 & 2000 Morrison Leahy Music Ltd, London W2 1QD

30 I Want Your Sex (Part III 'A Last Request')

It's late, time for bed
So I sit and I wait
For that gin and tonic to go to your head
I know it's a devious plan
But it's the only way that I know
To get those big bad car keys out of your hand

You know that I remain a gentleman
But even so there's only so much
A gentleman can stand

Sleep with me
Oh sleep with me tonight

My cards are on the table
My dreams are in your bed
Oh, if I was able
I'd be there instead
Sleep with me tonight

Words and Music by George Michael

31 I'm Your Man

Call me good, call me bad
Call me anything you want to baby
But I know that you're sad
And I know I'll make you happy
With the one thing that you never had
Baby I'm your man
Don't you know that
Baby I'm your man
You bet!

If you're gonna do it
Do it right, right?
Do it with me
If you're gonna do it
Do it right, right?
Do it with me
If you're gonna do it
Do it right, right?
Do it with me
If you're gonna do it
Do it right

So good, you're divine
Wanna take you, wanna make you
But they tell me it's a crime
Everybody knows
Where the good people go
But where we're going baby
Ain't no such word as no
Baby I'm your man
Don't you know who I am
Baby I'm your man
You bet!

If you gonna do it
Do it right, right?
Do it with me
If you're gonna do it
Do it right, right?
Do it with me
If you're gonna do it
Do it right, right?
Do it with me
If you're gonna do it
Do it right

To do it on my own first class information
I'll be your sexual inspiration
And with some stimulation
We can do it right

So why waste time with the other guys
When you can have mine
I ain't asking for no sacrifice
Baby your friends do not need to know
I've got a real nice place to go
I don't need you to care
I don't need you to understand
All I want is for you to be there
And when I'm turned on
If you want me
I'm your man

If you're gonna do it
Do it right, right?
Do it with me
If you're gonna do it
Do it right, right?
Do it with me
If you're gonna do it
You know what I say?
If you're gonna do it
Don't throw it away
Don't throw it baby

Because
I'll be your boy, I'll be your man
I'll be the one who understands
I'll be your first, I'll be your last
I'll be the only one you ask
I'll be your friend, I'll be your toy
I'll be the one who brings you joy
I'll be your hope, I'll be your pearl
I'll take you half way round the world!
I'll make you rich, I'll make your poor
Just don't use the door
Do it with me . . .

Words and Music by George Michael

32   If You Were My Woman

If you were my woman
And I was your man
There'd be no other woman
You'd be weak as a lamb
If you had the strength
To walk out that door
My love would over-rule my sense
I'd call you back for more
If you were my woman
If you were my woman
And I was your man

He tears you down darlin'
Says you're nothing at all
But I'll be there for you darlin'
When he lets you fall
You're like a diamond
But he treats you like glass
Yet you beg him to love you
With me you don't ask

If you were my woman
If you were my woman
If you were my woman
Here's what I'd do, oh
I'd never, no, no, no
Stop lovin' you

Life is so crazy
And love is so unkind
Because he came first darlin'
Will he hang on your mind
You're a part of me
And you don't even know it
I'm what you need
But I'm too afraid to show it

If you were my woman
If you were my woman
If you were my woman
Here's what I would do, oh
I'd never, no, no, no . . .

Words and Music by Clare McMurray, Pamela Sawyer and Leon Ware

33   It Doesn't Really Matter

It doesn't really matter that I love you
How many reasons call?
It doesn't really matter at all

It doesn't matter that I failed
To break down your father's wall
It really doesn't matter at all

Why tell me that you don't understand
When you do?
I thought I had something to say
But it really doesn't matter at all
It really doesn't matter at all
It really doesn't matter

I changed my name
To be rid of the things
That I want from you
It is strange
But a name is a name
And the truth is the truth

There is always
Always someone there to remind me
So I learned to live with shame
Tell myself I feel no pain
But I do
And if I have to tell you
Then it really doesn't matter at all
It really doesn't matter at all
It really doesn't matter
It doesn't matter at all

Loving you less, promises, promises
And it's no good looking back
Because time is a thief
And I believe that I'm too old for that
We're just saying the things
That we have said forever

It doesn't really matter that I love you
How many seasons fall?
It's too bad
It really doesn't matter at all
It really doesn't matter all
It really doesn't matter

Words and Music by George Michael

34 It's Alright With Me _____

Instrumental

Words and Music by Cole Porter

35 Jesus To A Child _____

Kindness in your eyes
I guess you heard me cry
You smiled at me
Like Jesus to a child

I'm blessed I know
Heaven sent, heaven stole
You smiled at me
Like Jesus to a child

And what have I learned
From all this pain?
I thought I'd never feel the same
About anyone or anything again

But now I know
When you find love
When you know that it exists
Then the lover that you miss
Will come to you
On those cold, cold nights
When you've been loved
When you know it holds such bliss
Then the lover that you kissed
Will comfort you
When there's no hope in sight

Sadness in my eyes
No-one guess
Well no-one tried
You smiled at me
Like Jesus to a child

Loveless and cold
With your last breath
You saved my soul
You smiled at me
Like Jesus to a child

And what have I learned
From all these tears?
I've waited for you
All those years
But just when it began
He took your love away

But I still say
When you find love
When you know that it exists
Then the lover that you miss
Will come to you
On those cold, cold nights
When you've been loved
When you know it holds such bliss
Then the lover that you kissed
Will comfort you
When there's no hope in sight

So the words you could not say
I'll sing them for you
And the love we would have made
I'll make it for two
For every single memory
Has become a part of me
You will always be my love

Well I've been loved
So I know just what love is
And the lover that I kissed
Is always by my side
Oh the lover I still miss
Was Jesus to a child

Words and Music by George Michael

36   Killer/Papa Was A Rolling Stone

So you want to be free?
To live your life
The way you want to be
Will you give if we cry?
Will we live or will we die?

Tainted hearts heal with time
Shoot that love
So we can stop the bleeding

Solitary brother
Is there still a part of you
That wants to live?
Solitary sister
Is there still a part of you
That wants to give?

It was the third of September
The day I'll always remember, yes I will
Because that was the day that my daddy died
I never had a chance to see him
No never heard nothing

But bad things about him
Mama I'm depending on you
To tell me the truth

My Mama just hung her head and said
Papa was a rolling stone
Wherever he laid his hat was his home
And when he died
All he left us was alone
But my Mama she said
Yeah oh my Mama said
Wherever he laid his hat was his home
And when he died
All he left us, all he left us
Can you believe he left us all alone

37   Kissing A Fool

You are far
When I could have been your star
You listened to people
Who scared you to death and from my heart
Strange that you were strong enough
To even make a start
But you'll never find peace of mind
Till you listen to your heart

People
You can never change the way they feel
Better let them do just what they will
For they will
If you let them steal your heart from you
People
Will always make a lover feel a fool
But you knew I loved you
We could have shown them all
We should have seen love through

Fooled me with the tears in your eyes
Covered me with kisses and lies
So goodbye
But please don't take my heart

You are far
I'm never gonna be your star
I'll pick up the pieces and mend my heart
Maybe I'll be strong enough
I don't know where to start
But I'll never find peace of mind
While I listen to my heart

People
You can never change the way they feel
Better let them do just what they will
For they will
If you let them steal your heart
People
Will always make a lover feel a fool
But you knew I loved you
We could have shown them all

But remember this
Every other kiss that you ever give
Long as we both live
When you need the hand of another man
One you really can surrender with
I will wait for you like I always do
There's something there
That can't compare with any other

You are far
When I could have been your star
You listened to people
Who scared you to death and from my heart
Strange that I was wrong enough
To think you'd love me too
Guess you were kissing a fool
You must have been kissing a fool

38   Look At Your Hands _____

I loved you once but look at you now
You're in somebody else's bed
I loved you once so I don't know how
You're with a man like that
You'd be better off dead
He don't care
He don't treat you right
It's not fair
I still want you at night
Can't you see you made a mistake girl
But he treats you like dirt
And I hate it

Lady, look at your hands
You got two fat children
And a drunken man
Betcha don't, betcha don't
Betcha don't like your life
Betcha don't, betcha don't
Betcha don't like it

Baby, look at your hands
You should have been my woman
When you had the chance
Betcha don't, betcha don't
Betcha don't like your life
Betcha don't, betcha don't
Betcha don't like your life now

He hits you once, be hits you twice
He don't care about the blood on his hands
But that's O.K. 'cause it's his wife
It's the only thing she understands
He says
Say you're gonna leave him
Say you're gonna try
But you're only talking
Oh I know you think I'm a young boy
But I'm good and I think we can make it

Lady, look at your hands
You got two fat children
And a drunken man
Betcha don't, betcha don't
Betcha don't like your life
Betcha don't, betcha don't
Betcha don't like it

Baby, look at your hands
You should have been my woman
When you had the chance
Betcha don't, betcha don't
Betcha don't like your life
Betcha don't, betcha don't
Betcha don't like your life now
Don't like your guy now

Well excuse me baby
But it's making me mad
The only one you wanted
Is the only one you'll never have
Betcha don't, betcha don't
Betcha don't like your life
Betcha don't, betcha don't
Betcha don't like it

Lady, look at your hands
You've got two fat children
And a drunken man
And I bet you don't like your life now

Words and Music by George Michael and David Austin

39 Miss Sarajevo

Is there a time for keeping your distance
A time to turn your eyes away?
Is there a time for keeping your head down
For getting on with your day?

Is there a time for kohl and lipstick
A time for cutting hair?
Is there a time for high street shopping
To find the right dress to wear?

Here she comes
Heads turn around
Here she comes
To take her crown

Is there a time to run for cover
A time for kiss and tell?
Is there a time for different colours
Different names you find it hard to spell?

Is there a time for first communion
A time for East Seventeen?
Is there a time to turn to Mecca
Is there time to be a beauty queen?

Here she comes
Heads turn around
Here she comes
Surreal in her crown

Here she comes
Heads turn around
Here she comes

Is there a time for tying ribbons
A time for Christmas trees?
Is there a time for laying tables
And the night is set to freeze?

Words and Music by Brian Eno, Bono, The Edge, Adam Clayton
and Larry Mullen Jnr

© 1995 Opal Music (for the world), London W11 3EQ,
Blue Mountain Music Ltd
(for the UK), London W11 3BU/Mother Music Limited (for the Republic
of Ireland), Dublin 2/
PolyGram International Music Publishing B.V. (for the rest of the world),
London SW1Y 4JU

40 A Moment With You

You can't keep a-holding it in
When it's something good

Hey, this won't take much time
We won't touch, we'll just wait for signs
And nothing was further from my mind
Than this moment with you

Woh, but if you'd only told me baby
I would have made some other plans
If I'd only seen it sooner
But what a way with your hands you had
I wanted that moment with you

I know that it's wrong
'If you need me I'm here'
Turns me on
I can't help thinking it's a miracle you're here
I can't help thinking it's a miracle

Say, you don't waste much time
We don't touch do we baby?
But still my hands are tied
For that moment with you

Woh, but if you'd only told me baby
I would have made some other plans
If I'd only seen it sooner
But what a way with your hands you had
I wanted that moment with you

You know that I'm strong
I've no reason to fear
Am I wrong?
I can't help thinking it's a miracle you're here
I can't help thinking it's a miracle

I can't help thinking it's a miracle
I can't help thinking it's a miracle
I can't help thinking it's a miracle you're here

You can't keep a-holding it in
When it's something good
(Get up, get up)
And a-who can you trust?
Dealing out justice with a minimum of fuss
You can't keep a-holding it in
When it's something good

Words and Music by George Michael

© 1998 & 2000 Dick Leahy Music Ltd, London W2 1QD

41   Monkey

Why can't you do it
Why can't you set your monkey free?
Always giving in to it
Do you love the monkey
Or do you love me?
Why can't you do it
Why do I have to share my baby
With a monkey?

Oh I count to ten
But I don't know how
And I don't know when
To open my eyes
If you kiss me again
Like you did just now
Like you did just then

I've had the rest
Now it's time I had the best
So you tell me that you won't do it any more
Well I'd write your heart a letter
But I think you know better
If I keep on asking baby
Maybe I'll get what I'm asking for

Why can't you do it
Why can't you set your monkey free?
Always giving in to it
Do you love the monkey
Or do you love me?
Why can't you do it
Why do I have to share my baby
With a monkey?

Oh I hate your friends
But I don't know how
And I don't know when
To open your eyes
Yes your monkey's back again
Do you want him now
Like you did back then?

I tried my best
But your head is such a mess
So I guess that I don't want you anymore
Well you say you care about me
That you just can't do without me
But you keep on dancing baby
Till that monkey has you on the floor

Why can't you do it
Why can't you set your monkey free?
Always giving in to it
Do you love the monkey
Or do you love me?
Why can't you do it
Why do I have to share my baby
With a monkey?

Don't look now
There's a monkey on your back
Don't look now
There's a monkey on your back

So you tell me that you won't do any more
If I keep on asking baby
Maybe I'll get what I'm asking for

Why can't you do it
Why can't you set your monkey free?
Always giving in to it
Do you love the monkey
Or do you love me?
Why can't you do it
Why do I have to share my baby
With a monkey?

Words and Music by George Michael

42 Mother's Pride

Oh she knows, she takes his hand
And prays the child will understand
At the door they watch the men go by
In the clothes that daddy wore

Mother's pride, baby boy
His father's eyes
He's a soldier waiting for a war
Time will come, he'll hold a gun
His father's son

And as he grows he hears the band
Takes the step from boy to man
At the shore she waves her son goodbye
Like the man she did before

Mother's pride, just a boy
His country's eyes
He's a soldier waving at the shore

And in her heart
The time has come to lose a son

And all the husbands, all the sons
All the lovers gone
They make no difference
No difference in the end
Still hear the women say
Your daddy died a hero
In the name of God and man

Mother's pride, crazy boy
His lifeless eyes
He's a soldier now for ever more
He'll hold a gun till kingdom come

Words and Music by George Michael

© 1990 & 2000 Morrison Leahy Music Ltd, London W2 1QD

43 Move On

I've been in and out of favour with lady luck
I gotta tell ya
I've seen things I never wanted to see
I've got to get back on my feet
I feel like I've been sleeping
Sweet sweet time
Has been a real good friend of mine

Waiting for that change of season
Ah the winter's been so long
Searching for that rhyme or reason
You've just got to move on
Hold it together, move on
Life's so short, move on
Only time will set you free
Just like me, so move on
You put your fears behind you
You better get yourself
Where you want to be
I think of all the days and nights
I've spent crying
And I move on

Because I've been in and out of favour with love
I gotta tell ya
I've been things I never wanted to be
And then some angel called me up
And told me I was sleeping
Don't waste time
'Cause even angels say goodbye

Waiting for that change of season
Ah the winter's been so long
Searching for that rhyme or reason
You've just got to move on

Hold it together, move on
Life's so short, move on
Only time will set you free
Just like me, so move on
You put your fears behind you
You better get yourself
Where you want to be
I think of all the days and nights
I've spent crying endlessly

And oh there goes another season
Getting hard to find a decent song to play
But oh I guess I've got my reasons
Everybody thinks I'm doing A-OK
They ought to know by now

Oh that such a thing should
Make a mock of your life
And don't you think that maybe
Moving on is good advice?

Move on, I tell you, move on
Hold it together, move on
Life's so short, move on
And life she won't wait for me, move on

Put your fears behind you
You better get yourself
Where you wanna be
I think of all the days and nights
That I spent crying
Until my angel set me free
I'm gonna be lucky in love some day

Words and Music by George Michael

© 1995 & 1999 Dick Leahy Music Ltd, London W2 1QD

44 My Baby Just Cares For Me ____

My baby don't care for shows
My baby don't care for clothes
My baby just cares for me
My baby don't care for cars and races
My baby don't care for
He don't care for high tone places

Elizabeth Taylor is not his style
And even Ricky Martin's smile
Is something he can't see
My baby don't care who knows it
My baby just cares for me

I wonder what's wrong with baby
My baby just cares for
He just says his prayers for
I say baby just cares for me

Words by Gus Kahn
Music by Walter Donaldson

45 Older _____

I should have known, it seemed too easy
You were there and I was breathing blue
Strange, baby
Don't you think I'm looking older?
And something good has happened to me
Change is a stranger
You have yet to know

Well you're out of time, I'm letting go
You'll be fine, well that much I know
You're out of time, I'm letting go
I'm not the man you want

I should have known, it seemed so easy
You were there, I thought I needed you
Strange, baby
Don't you think I'm looking older
But something good has happened to me
Change is a stranger
Who never seems to show

So you're out of time, I'm letting go
You'll be fine or maybe you won't
You're out of time, I'm letting go
I'm not the man that you want

I never should have looked back
In your direction
I know that
Just the same old fights again baby
There are wasted days
Without affection
I'm not that foolish anymore

So you're out of time, I'm letting go
You'll be fine, well that much I know
You're out of time, I'm letting go
I'm not the man that you want

Words and Music by George Michael

46   One More Try

I've had enough of danger
And people on the streets
I'm looking out for angels
Just trying to find some peace
Now I think it's time
That you let me know
So if you love me, say you love me
But if you don't, just let me go

'Cause teacher there are things
That I don't want to learn
And the last one I had made me cry
So I don't wanna learn to
Hold you, touch you
Think that you're mine
Because it ain't no joy
For an uptown boy
Whose teacher has told him goodbye

When you were just a stranger
And I was at your feet
I didn't feel the danger
Now I feel the heat
That look in your eyes
Telling me no
So you think that you love me
Know that you need me
I wrote the song, I know it's wrong
Just let me go . . .

And teacher there are things
That I don't want to learn
The last one I had made me cry
So I don't wanna learn to
Hold you, touch you
Think that you're mine
Because it ain't no joy
For an uptown boy
Whose teacher has told him goodbye

So when you say that you need me
That you'll never leave me
I know you're wrong
You're not that strong
Let me go

And teacher there are things
That I still have to learn
But the one thing I have is my pride
Oh so I don't want to learn to
Hold you, touch you
Think that you're mine
Because there ain't no joy
For an uptown boy
Who just isn't willing to try
I'm so cold inside
Maybe just one more try

Words and Music by George Michael

47   Outside

I think I'm done with the sofa
I think I'm done with the hall
I think I'm done with the kitchen table baby

Let's go outside
In the sunshine
I know you want to
But you can't say yes
Let's go outside
In the moonshine
Take me to the places
That I love best

So my angel she says
Don't you worry
'Bout the things they're saying
Got no friends in high places
And the game that you gave away
Wasn't worth playing

Let's go outside
In the sunshine
I know you want to
But you can't say yes
Let's go outside
In the meantime
Take me to the places
That I love best

And yes, I've been bad
Doctor won't you do with me what you can
You see I think about it all the time
Twenty-four seven

You say you want it, you got it
I never really said it before
There's nothing here but flesh and bone
There's nothing more, nothing more
There's nothing more
Back to nature
Just human nature
Getting back to . . .

I think I'm done with the sofa
I think I'm done with the hall
I think I'm done with the kitchen table baby

Let's go outside
In the sunshine
I know you want to
But you can't say yes
Let's go outside
In the moonshine
Take me to the places
That I love best

And yes, I've been bad
Doctor won't you do with me what you can
You see I think about it all the time
I'd service the community
(But I already have you see!)

I never really said it before
There's nothing here but flesh and bone
There's nothing more, nothing more
There's nothing more

Back to nature
Just human nature
Dancing on the D-train baby
When the moon is high
And the grass is jumpin'
Come on, just keep on funkin'

Words and Music by George Michael

48 Praying For Time

These are the days of the open hand
They will not be the last
Look around now
These are the days
Of the beggars and choosers
This is the year of the hungry man
Whose place is in the past
Hand in hand with ignorance
And legitimate excuses

The rich declare themselves poor
And most of us are not sure
If we have too much
But we'll take our chances
'Cause God's stopped keeping score
I guess somewhere along the way
He must have let us all out to play
Turned His back and all God's children
Crept out the back door

And it's hard to love
There's so much to hate
Hanging on to hope
When there is no hope to speak of
And the wounded skies above
Say it's much, much too late
Well maybe we should all be praying for time

These are the days of the empty hand
You hold on to what you can
And charity is a coat
You wear twice a year
This is the year of the guilty man
Your television takes a stand
And you find that what was over there
Is over here

So you scream from behind your door
Say what's mine is mine and not yours
I may have too much
But I'll take my chances
'Cause God's stopped keeping score
And you cling to the things they sold you
Did you cover your eyes when they told you
That he can't come back
'Cause he has no children to come back for

And it's hard to love
There's so much to hate
Hanging on to hope
When there is no hope to speak of
And the wounded skies above
Say it's much too late
So maybe we should all be praying for time

Words and Music by George Michael

© 1989 & 2000 Morrison Leahy Music Ltd, London W2 1QD

49 Roxanne

Roxanne, you don't have to put on the red light
Those days are over
You don't have to sell your body to the night

Roxanne, you don't have to wear that dress tonight
Walk the streets for money
You don't care if it's wrong or if it's right

Roxanne, you don't have to put on the red light
Roxanne, you don't have to

I loved you since I knew you
I wouldn't talk down to you
I have to tell you just how I feel
I won't share you with another boy

I know my mind is made up
So put away your make-up
I told you once, I won't tell you again
It's a bad way

Roxanne, you don't have to put on the red light
Roxanne, don't you know, you don't have to
Baby don't put it on

Words and Music by Sting

© 1978 G.M. Sumner.
EMI Music Publishing Ltd/Magnetic Publishing Ltd, London WC2H 0EA

50 Safe

Sweet thing, I know how strong that I appear
But you don't know the days
        since somebody loved me
I stopped waiting, you came
And led me through that door again
You say you want to stay
But you don't know me, no you don't know

You make me feel safe

Someday, my darkest fears will find their way
After all, somebody loves me, loves me
All day, my heart tells strangers how I feel
And it's hard not to feel this way
When you thought your future was on prescription

You make me feel safe

Words and Music by George Michael

© 1995 & 2000 Dick Leahy Music Ltd, London W2 1QD

51 Secret Love

Once I had a secret love
That lived within the heart of me
All too soon my secret love
Became impatient to be free

So I told a friendly star
The way that dreamers often do
Just how wonderful you are
And why I'm so in love with you

Now I shout it from the highest hills
Even told the golden daffodils
At last my heart's an open door
And my secret love's no secret anymore
My secret love's no secret
My secret love's no secret anymore

Words and Music by Sammy Fain and Paul Francis Webster

© 1953 Remick Music Corp, USA
Warner/Chappell Music Ltd, London W6 8BS

52 Somebody To Love

Each morning I get up I die a little
Can't barely stand on my feet
Take a look in the mirror
And cry 'Lord what are you doing to me?'
I've spent all my years in believing you
But I just can't get no relief, Lord

Somebody, somebody
Can anybody find me somebody to love?

I work hard everyday of my life
I work till I ache my bones
At the end of the day
I take home my hard-earned pay all on my own
I go down on my knees and I start to pray
Till the tears run down from my eyes
Lord somebody (somebody)
Can anybody find me somebody to love?

He works hard every day
I try and I try and I try
But everybody wants to put me down
They say I'm going crazy
They say I've got a lot of water on my brain

Ain't got no common sense
He's got nobody left to believe in
Yeah, yeah, yeah, yeah
Ooh somebody, somebody
Can anybody find me somebody to love?

I got no feel, I got no rhythm
I just keep losing my beat
I'm alright, I'm alright
I ain't gonna face no defeat
I just gotta get out of this prison cell
Some day I'm gonna be free, Lord

Find me somebody to love
Find me somebody to love
Somebody, somebody, somebody find me
Somebody find me somebody to love
Can anybody find me somebody to love?
Find me somebody to love

Words and Music by Freddie Mercury

© 1976 & 2000 Queen Music Ltd/EMI Music Publishing Ltd,
London WC2H 0EA

53 Something To Save

If you've got something to say
Why don't you say it?
If you've got something to give
Why don't you give it to me?
Day after day I have to say it
We're moving further from heaven
And closer to the deep blue sea

'Cause I have no secrets from you
And I have nothing left to hide
And I'm open to all your questions
Why can't you reach inside
Like I have, like I have for you

And all these games that you play
Don't tell me how a man should be
Some would say if you knew
You wouldn't be here with me
I love you, I still love you
But I guess it's time to let you be
'Cause I have no secrets from you
And I have nothing left to hide
And I'm so tired of all these questions
'Cause maybe you just changed your mind
Like I have, like I have

When I was at your doorstep
You told me to look around
Said come in, you and your heart sit down
But you better watch your step
'Cause you're not far from the ground
And one fine day this all falls down
Like I have

If you've got something to say
Why don't you say it?
If you've got something to give
Why don't you give it to me?
Day after day I have to say it
If we've got something to save
Why don't we save it?

Words and Music by George Michael

© 1988 & 2000 Morrison Leahy Music Ltd, London W2 1QD

54 Soul Free

Higher and higher won't you come with me
Baby gonna get my soul free, soul free

Now you and me, I guess
We see things differently
We're night and day
A bad connection some would say
And I don't want nothing to change
I don't want nothing to change
And I don't want nothing to change
No, no, no because

When you touch me baby
I don't have no choice
Oh that sweet temptation in your voice

Higher, higher won't you come with me
Baby gonna get my soul free, soul free

Now seems to me
Some things have just got to be
The games we play
Make up, break up day by day
And I don't want nothing to change
I don't want nothing to change
Said I don't want nothing to change
No, no, no because

When you touch me baby
I don't have no choice
Oh that sweet temptation in your voice

Higher, higher won't you come with me
Baby gonna get my soul free, soul free

When you touch me baby
I don't have no choice
Oh that sweet temptation in your voice

Words and Music by George Michael

© 1990 & 2000 Morrison Leahy Music Ltd, London W2 1QD

55   Spinning The Wheel _____

Spinning the wheel
Spinning the wheel

Five o'clock in the morning
You ain't home
I can't help thinking that's strange
Baby I just want you to know
I won't go through it again
Those clouds are closing in
And I will not accept this
As a part of my life
I will not live in fear of what may be
And the lessons I have learned with you
I would rather be alone than watch you
Spinning that wheel for me

You've got a thing about danger
Ain't you getting what you want from me?
You've got a thing about strangers
Baby that's what we used to be
You've got a thing about danger baby
I guess the hungry just can't see
One of these days you're gonna
Bring some home to me

Six o'clock in the morning
You ain't phoned
I can't help thinking that's strange
It seems that everybody takes their chances
These days, oh yeah

We're standing in the rain
And I will not accept this
As a part of my life
I will not live in fear of what may be
And the lessons I have learned with you
I would rather be alone than watch you
Spinning that wheel for me

You've got a thing about danger
Ain't you getting what you want from me?
You've got a thing about strangers
Baby that's what we used to be
You've got a thing about danger baby
I guess the hungry just can't see
One of these days you're gonna
Bring some home to me

How can you love me
When you're playing with my life?
You say give me time and I'll do better I swear
Give me time and I'll lead you back to despair
And I don't want to go back there
I don't want to go back there
I'm never going back to that
And that's a fact baby!
One of these days you're gonna
Bring some home to me

Words and Music by George Michael and Johnny Douglas

56   Star People _____

Maybe your mama gave you up boy
Maybe your daddy didn't love you enough girl

Star people
Counting your money
Until your soul turns green
Star people
Counting the cost
Of your desire to be seen

I do not count myself among you
I may be living in a dream
It's just there seems so many of you
Can't help but hope there's a difference
Between you and me

You're a star
You're a star

I said maybe your mama gave you up boy
It's the same old same old
Maybe your daddy didn't love you enough girl

Star people
Never forget your secret's safe with me
Just look at all the wonderful people
Trying to forget they had to pay for what you see
It's a dream with a nightmare stuck in the middle
But listen brother where would you be
Without all of this attention?
You'd die, I'd die
We'd die wouldn't we?
Well wouldn't we?

You're a star
You're a star
I said maybe your mama gave you up boy
It's the same old same old
Maybe your daddy didn't love you enough girl

You only wanted them to love you
May have been living in a dream
And as the demons tower above you
You bite your tongue
When you really want to scream

You're a star
Talk about your mother
Talk about your father
Talk about the people
Who have made you what you are
Talk about your teacher
The bully boy who beat you
Talk about the people who have paid
For that new sports car

You're a big, bad star
Look at you
Say how much is enough?
Did you get off on a bad foot baby?
Do you have a little tale to tell?
Did you get off on a bad foot, a bad, bad foot?
Is that why you're a star?
Is that what makes a star?
Say how much is enough
Well nothing comes from nothing baby
That fame and fortune's heaven sent
And who gives a fuck about your problems darling
'Cause you can pay the rent?
How much is enough?

Words and Music by George Michael

© 1994 & 2000 Dick Leahy Music Ltd, London W2 1QD

57 The Strangest Thing _____

Take my life
Time has been twisting the knife
I don't recognise people I care for
Take my dreams
Childish and weak at the seams
Please don't analyse
Please just be there for me
The things that I know
Nobody told me
The seeds that are sown
They still control me

There's a liar in my head
There's a thief upon my bed
And the strangest thing
Is I cannot seem to get my eyes off you

Give me something I can hold
Give me something to believe in
I am frightened for my soul
Please, please make love to me
Send love to me
Send love through me
Heal me with your cry
The only one who ever knew me
We've wasted so much time

Take my hand
Lead me to some perfect land
That I cannot find inside my head

Wake me with love
It's all, all I need
But in all this time
Still no-one says
If I had not asked
Would you have told me?
If you call this love
Why don't you hold me?

There's a liar in my head
There's a thief upon my bed
And the strangest thing
Is I cannot seem to get my eyes off you

Give me something I can hold
Give me something to believe in
I am frightened for my soul
Please, please make love to me
Send love to me
Send love through me
Heal me with your cry
The only one who ever knew me
We've wasted so much time

Words and Music by George Michael

© 1994 & 2000 Dick Leahy Music Ltd, London W2 1QD

58   These Are The Days Of Our Lives

Sometimes I get to feelin'
I was back in the old days
Long ago
When we were kids
When we were young
Things seemed so perfect
You know?

The days were endless
We were crazy, we were young
The sun was always shining
We just lived for fun
Sometimes it seems like lately
I just don't know
The rest of my life's been just a show

Those were the days of our lives
The bad things in life were so few
Those days are all gone now
But one thing is true
When I look and I find
I still love you

You can't turn back the clock
You can't turn back the tide
Ain't that a shame?
I'd like to go back one time
On a roller coaster ride
When life's just a game

No use in sitting
And a-thinking on what you did
When you can lay back
And enjoy it through your kids
Sometimes it seems like lately
I just don't know
Better sit back
And go with the flow

These are the days of our lives
They've flown in the swiftness of time
Those days are all gone now
But some things remain
When I look and I find
No change

Those were the days of our lives
The bad things in life were so few
Those days are all gone now
But one thing's still true
When I look and I find
I still love you

Words and Music by Queen

© 1991 & 2000 Queen Music Ltd/EMI Music Publishing Ltd,
London WC2H 0EA

59   They Won't Go When I Go _____

No more lying friends
Wanting tragic ends
Though they do pretend
They won't go when I go

All those bleeding hearts
With sorrows to impart
Were right here from the start
They won't go when I go

And I'll go where I've longed to go
So long away from tears

Gone from painful cries
Away from saddened eyes
Along with him I'll bide
They won't go when I go

Big men feeling small
Weak ones standing tall
I will watch them fall
They won't go when I go

And I'll go where I've longed to go
So long away from tears

Unclean minds lead the pure
The innocent will leave for sure
For them there is a resting place
People sinning just for fun
They will never see the sun
For they can never show their faces
There ain't no room for the hopeless sinner
Who will take more than he will give
He will give, he will give
He ain't hardly gonna give

The greed of man will be
Far away from me
And my soul will be free
They won't go when I go

Since my soul conceived
All that I believe
The kingdom I will see
They won't go when I go

And I go where I'll go
No-one can keep me
From my destiny

Words and Music by Stevie Wonder and Yvonne Wright

© 1974 & 2000 Black Bull Music Inc and Jobete Music Co Inc, USA
Black Bull Music/Jobete Music Co Inc, London WC2H 0EA

60   To Be Forgiven

I'm going down
Won't you help me?
Save me from myself
I hear a sound of a memory
Maybe time will tell

Suddenly my life
Is like a river
Taking me places
I don't wanna go
But like all good men
Who swim too well
It takes all that I have
Just to cry for help
Then that voice in my head
Tells me no

I'm going down
Wont you help me?
Save me from myself
I look around for a fantasy
Maybe, who can tell

Let me live my life
Beside the river
Take me to places
Where a child can grow
And then maybe, maybe
The boy inside me
Will forsake me
Maybe the child in me
Will just let me go

I'm going down
Cold, cold water
Is rushing in
I'm going down
And I would beg
To be forgiven
If I knew myself
If I knew myself
Save me, save me
I'm going down
I'm going down

Words and Music by George Michael

61   Too Funky

Hey you're just too funky for me
I've got to get inside of you
And I'll show you heaven if you'll let me
Hey you're just too funky for me
I've got to get inside
I've got to get inside of you

I've watched your fingers working overtime
I've got to thinking that they should be mine
I'd love to see you naked baby
I'd like to think that sometime
Maybe tonight if that's alright

Hey you're just too funky for me
I've got to get inside of you
And I'll show you heaven if you'll let me
Hey you're just too funky for me
I've got to get inside
I've got to get inside of you
I watch you drinking and I take my time

I watch you sinking all that cheap red wine
I've got to see you naked baby
I'd like to think that sometime
Maybe tonight my goal's in sight

Baby, why do you do this to me?
Won't let you go
You're such a, you're such a
Baby, why do you do this to me?
I've got to know

(Gonna be the kind of lover that you never had)
Hey you're just too funky
(You're never gonna have another lover in your bed)
You're just too funky for me

(Would you like me to seduce you?
Is that what you're trying to tell me?)
Everybody wants a lover like that
Everybody wants a lover like that
(Is that what you're trying to tell me?)
Everybody wants a lover like that
(Would you like me to seduce you?
You're such a, you're such a
(Would you like me to seduce you?)

Would you stop playing with that radio of yours
I'm trying to get some sleep

Words and Music by George Michael

62   Waiting For That Day _____

So every day I see you in some other face
They crack a smile, talk a while
Try to take your place
My memory serves me far too well
I just sit here on this mountain
Thinking to myself
You're a fool boy
Why don't you go down
Find somebody, find somebody else
My memory serves me far too well

It's not as though we just broke up
It's not as though it was yesterday
But something I just can't explain
Something in me needs this pain
I know I'll never see your face again
C'mon now, c'mon now
I've got to be strong now

Now everybody's talking about this new decade
Like you say the magic numbers
Then just say goodbye
       to the stupid mistakes you made
Oh my memory serves me far too well

Don't you know that the years will come and go
Some of us will change our lives
Some of us still have nothing to show
Nothing baby but memories

And if these wounds they are self inflicted
I don't really know how
My poor heart could have protected me
But if I have to carry this pain
If you will not share the blame
I deserve to see your face again

You don't have to be so strong
Come back to me darling
I will make it worth your while
Come on back to your baby
I miss your kiss, I miss your smile
Seems to me the peace I search to find
Ain't gonna be mine until you say you will
Don't you keep me waiting for that day
I know, I know, I know
You hear these words that I say
C'mon now

Words and Music by George Michael

63   Waiting (Reprise) _____

There ain't no point in moving on
Till you've got somewhere to go
And the road that I have walked upon
Well it filled my pockets
And emptied out my soul

All those insecurities
That have held me down for so long
I can't say that I've found a cure for these
But at least I know them
So they're not so strong
You look for your dreams in heaven
But what the hell are you supposed to do
When they come true?

There's one year of my life in these songs
And some of them are about you
I know there's no way
I can right those wrongs
Believe me I would not lie

You've hurt my pride
And I guess there's a road without you
But you once said
There's a way back for every man
So here I am
Don't people change?
Here I am
Is it too late to try again?
Here I am

Words and Music by Dennis Morgan and Simon Climie

64 Waltz Away Dreaming

George Michael
I'm here if you see me

Toby Bourke
She's got a song in her head
And she'll sing to me
She's got a laugh
That reminds me of why she's in love with me
She'd never let show she was lonely
In case it had frightened me
She was carpet and stone
Independent alone
But this love always shone around me
Every time

Waltz away dreaming
Till your day begins
Again and again
Free from the seasons
And the state I'm in
And no I can't hold her
All under one love

It was so long ago
When we kissed in the streets
Now you fly like an eagle above
While I waltz away anyway
And I'm waltzing my days away
Searching for this woman I love

G.M.
I'm here if you see me

She had a history of joy and pain in time
And she chose to leave
She had a thousand and one photographs
That you would not believe
She'll come to you in disguise
She's there in your children's eyes
Still our mother
She's still your wife
So let her . . .

Both
Waltz away dreaming
Till your day begins
Free from the reasons
And this state I'm in

T.B.
And oh,
G.M.
Trust me she ain't going anywhere
T.B.
I can't hold it
All under one love
G.M.
Trust me, she told me
When you're ready she'll be there
T.B.
It was so long ago
G.M.
No, don't let go of her
Both
When we kissed in the streets
Now you fly like an eagle above
I'll waltz away anyway
T.B.
Then I'm be waltzing my days away
Searching for this woman I love

(And the moment you see me
I will live in your life
We will walk through my garden
I will see through your eyes) ·
T.B.
Waltzing my days away
G.M.
I was in despair till she found me there
Every grown man cries with his mother's eyes
And when you're ready too
She'll come back to you
She's waiting
T.B.
Waltzing my days away in despair
G.M.
Father, she's waiting

Words and Music by George Michael and Toby Bourke

65　Where Or When _____

It seems we stood and talked like this before
We looked at each other in the same way then
But I can't remember where or when
The clothes you're wearing are the clothes you wore
The smile that you are smiling you were smiling then
But I can't remember where or when

Some things that happen for the first time
Seem to be happening again and you know it
And so it seems that we have met before
And laughed before and loved before
But baby who knows where or when

Some things that happen for the first time
Seem to be happening again
And so it seems that we have met before
And laughed before and loved before
But who knows where or when

Words by Lorenz Hart
Music by Richard Rodgers

66　Wild Is The Wind _____

Love me, love me, love me
Say you do
Let me fly away with you
For my love is like the wind
And wild is the wind

Give me more than one caress
Satisfy this hungriness
Let the wind blow through your heart
And wild is the wind

You touch me
I hear the sounds of mandolins
You kiss me
With your kiss my life begins

You're Spring to me
All things to me
You're life itself

Like a leaf clings to the tree
Oh my darling, cling to me
For we're creatures of the wind
And wild is the wind

Words by Ned Washington
Music by Dimitri Tiomkin

67　You Have Been Loved _____

She takes the back road and the lane
Past the school that has not changed
In all this time
She thinks of when the boy was young
All the battles she had won
Just to give him life
That man, she loved that man
For all his life
And now we meet to take him flowers
And only God knows why

For what's the use of pressing palms
When children fade in mother's arms?
It's a cruel world

We've so much to lose
And what we have to learn
We rarely choose

So if it's God who took her son
He cannot be the one living in her mind
'Take care my love' she said
'Don't think that God is dead'
'Take care my love' she said
'You have been loved'

If I was weak, forgive me
But I was terrified
You brushed my eyes with angels' wings
Full of love
The kind that makes devils cry
So these days my life has changed
And I'll be fine
But she just sits and counts the hours
Searching for her crime

So what's the use in pressing palms
If you won't keep such love from harm?
It's a cruel world, you've so much to prove
And heaven help the ones who wait for you

Now I've no daughters, I've no sons
Guess I'm the only one living in my life
'Take care my love' he said
'Don't think that God is dead'
'Take care my love' he said
'You have been loved'

Words and Music by George Michael and David Austin

© 1996 Dick Leahy Music Ltd, London W2 1QD and
European Music Publishing Ltd/
BMG Music Publishing Ltd, London SW6 3JW

68   You Know That I Want To _____

Lover don't love too much
It's a bad thing, a sad thing
And it's heaven to the touch
Everybody's got some moment in their lives
They can't change
Don't think baby
I know you don't care
What's right or wrong
All that I know
Is that love don't belong here
And so it's better to turn the page
And watch me walk away my dear
Watch me walk away
But you say

I can't stop but you know that I want to
I can't stop don't you know that I want you?
I want you baby, more than ever
I can't stop but you know that I want to
I can't stop don't you know that I want you?
But it's never gonna be that easy child
I don't wanna waste your time

Lover don't love too much
I'm a bad boy, I'm a sad boy
And I never give you much
Everybody's got some moment in their lives
They can't change
So I do not dare to take you home
All that I know is
There's something so wrong with this heat
Why do you touch the flame?
You only feel the pain my dear
You always find it here
But you say

I can't stop but you know that I want to
I can't stop don't you know that I want you?
I want you baby, more than ever
I can't stop but you know that I want to
I can't stop don't you know that I want you?
But it's never gonna be

So it happens every time
It's so easy to forgive myself with a little wine
But you want more
And the the pleasure will be all mine
Can't you see, I'm using you baby?

I can't stop but you know that I want to
I can't stop don't you know that I want you?
I want you baby, more than ever
I can't stop but you know that I want to
I can't stop don't you know that I want you?
But it's never gonna be that easy

Words and Music by George Michael and Jonathan Douglas

© 1996 & 2000 Dick Leahy Music Ltd, London W2 1QD and
Rondor Music (London) Ltd, London SW6 4TW

69 You've Changed

You've changed
That sparkle in your eyes is gone
Your smile is just a careless yawn
You're breaking my heart
You've changed

You've changed
Your kisses now are so blasé
You're bored with me in every way
I can't understand
You've changed

You've forgotten the words 'I love you'
Each memory that we shared
You ignore every star above you
I can't realise that you ever cared

You've changed
You're not the angel I once knew
No need to tell me that we're through
It's all over now
You've changed
I miss you

Words by Bill Carey
Music by Carl Fischer

the **MUSIC**

1 As

Words and Music by Stevie Wonder

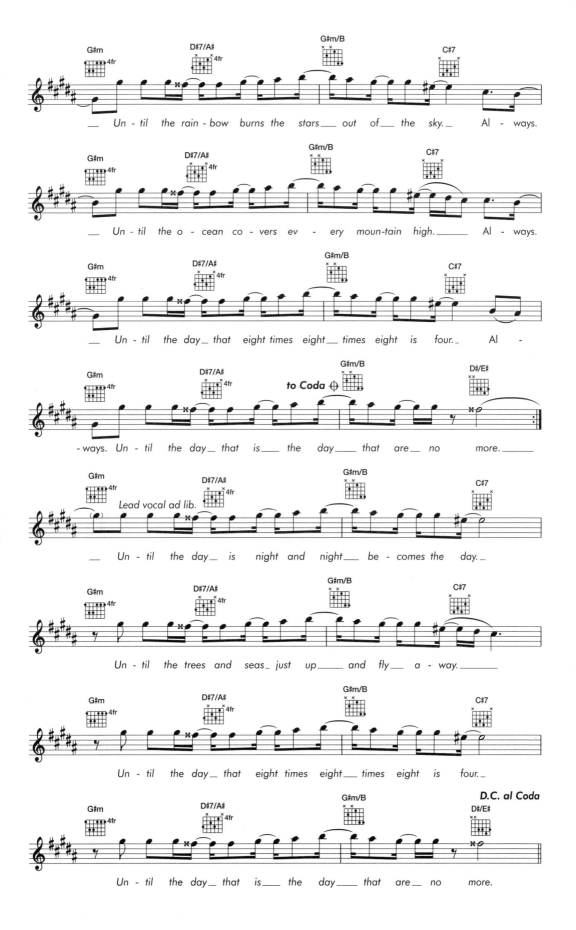

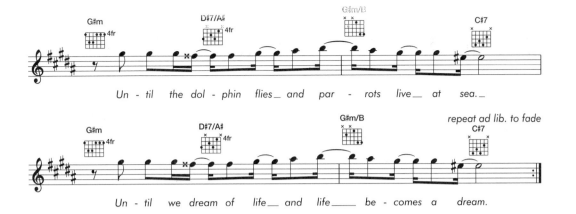

Un - til the dol - phin flies__ and par - rots live__ at sea.__

Un - til we dream of life__ and life____ be - comes a dream.

Mary Jo Blige
Did you know that true love asks for nothing
Her acceptance is the way we pay
Did you know that life has given love a guarantee
To last through forever another day

George Michael
As today I know I'm living but tomorrow could make the past
But that I mustn't fear 'cause you're here
M.J.B.
Now I know deep in my mind the love of me I've left behind
G.M.
And I'll be loving you always

Chorus
Until the rainbow burns the stars out of the sky
Until the ocean covers every mountain high
Until the dolphin flies and parrots live at sea
Until we dream of life and life becomes a dream

Until the day is night and night becomes the day
Until the trees and seas just up and fly away
Until the day that eight times eight times is four
Until the day that is the day that are no more

G.M.
Did you know that true love asks for nothing
Her acceptance is the way we pay
Did you know that life has given love a guarantee
To last through forever another day

As around the sun the earth knows she's revolving
And the rosebuds know to bloom in early May
M.J.B.
Now I know deep in my mind the love of me I've left behind
G.M.
And I'll be loving you always

Repeat Chorus to fade

2 Brother Can You Spare A Dime?

Words by E Y Harburg
Music by Jay Gorney

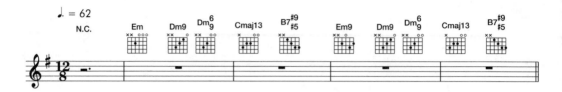

Once I built a rail - road,_ made_ it run,

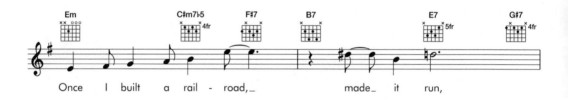

made_ it race_____ a - gainst time._____

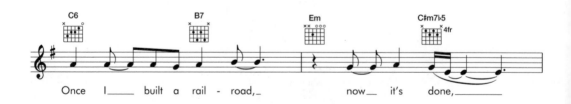

Once I_____ built a rail - road,_ now_ it's done,_____

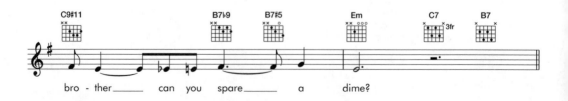

bro - ther_____ can you spare_____ a dime?

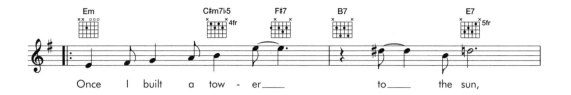

Once I built a tow - er___ to___ the sun,

brick___ and ri - vet___ and lime.___

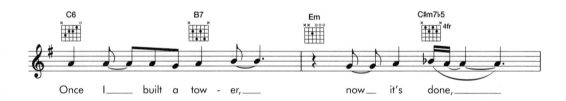

Once I___ built a tow - er,___ now___ it's done,___

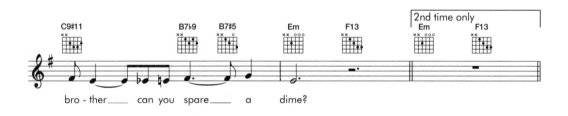

2nd time only

bro - ther___ can you spare___ a dime?

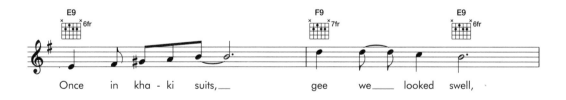

Once in kha - ki suits,___ gee we___ looked swell,

full___ of that Yan - kee___ Doo - dle___ de dum.

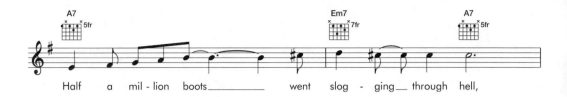

Half a mil - lion boots_____ went slog - ging_ through hell,

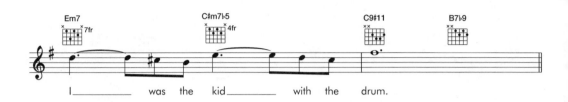

I_____ was the kid_____ with the drum.

Say don't you re - mem - ber_____ they called me Al,

it_____ was Al_____ all the time.

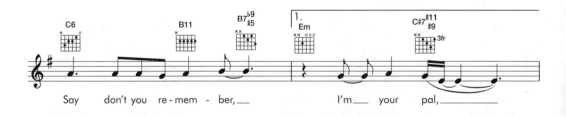

Say don't you re - mem - ber, _____ I'm_ your pal, _____

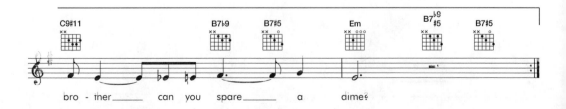

bro - ther_____ can you spare_____ a dime?

I'm_ your pal,_____ bro-ther___ can you spare___ a dime?

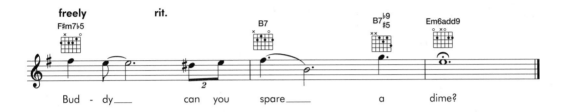

freely   **rit.**

Bud - dy____ can you spare_____ a dime?

Once in khaki suits, gee we looked swell
Full of that Yankee Doodle de dum
Half a million boots went slogging through hell
I was the kid with the drum

Say don't you remember they called me Al
It was Al all the time
Say don't you remember I'm your pal
Brother can you spare a dime?
Buddy can you spare a dime?

3 Calling You

Words and Music by Robert Eria Telson

♩ = 132

Capo 1

A₂maj7/C   D₂sus2#11

A de-sert road___ from Ve - gas to no - where,___

Fm9   B₂7sus4

some place bet - ter___ than_ where you've been.___

A₂maj7/C   D₂sus2#11

A cof-fee ma-chine___ that needs___ some fix-ing,___

Fm9   B₂7sus4   *repeat on 𝄌 only*

in a lit-tle ca-fé - just a - round___ the bend.___

D₂m6/F₂   E₂/D₂   Cm7₂5

I___ am call - - ing you._

F7   Dm7₂5   G7#5

_ Well can't you hear me? I___ am call -

A desert road from Vegas to nowhere
Some place better than where you've been
A coffee machine that needs some fixing
In a little café just around the bend

A hot, dry wind blows right through me
The baby's crying so I can't sleep
We both know a change is coming
Coming closer to . . .

I am calling you
Can't you hear me?
I am calling you
Ooh wo, no, no

Instrumental

A desert road from Vegas to nowhere

4 Careless Whisper

Words and Music by George Michael and Andrew Ridgeley

I feel so___ un - sure___ as I take your hand__ and lead you to the dance floor. As the mu - sic dies, some-thing in your eyes___ calls to mind a sil - ver screen and you're its sad good - bye. — I'm ne-ver gon-na dance a - gain, guil - ty feet have got__ no rhy - thm. Though it's ea - sy to pre-tend, I know you're not__ a fool.__ I

should have known bet-ter than to cheat a friend, and waste the chance that I've_ been gi - ven,

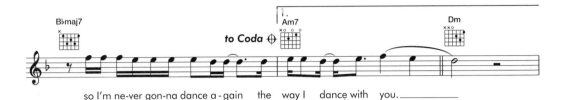

so I'm ne-ver gon-na dance a - gain the way I dance with you.____

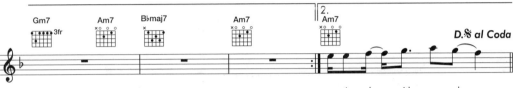

way I dance with you, oh.____

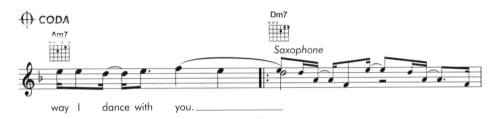

Saxophone

way I dance with you.____

repeat ad lib. to fade

Time can never mend
The careless whisper
Of a good friend
To the heart and mind
Ignorance is kind
There's no comfort in the truth
Pain is the heart you'll find

I'm never gonna dance again
Guilty feet have got no rhythm
Though its easy to pretend
I know you're not a fool
I should have known better
(Should have known better)
Than to cheat a friend
And waste the chance that I've been given
So I'm never gonna dance again
The way I dance with you, oh

Tonight the music seems so loud
I wish that we could lose this crowd
Maybe it's better this way
We'd hurt each other with the things we want to say
We could have been so good together
We could have lived this dance forever
But now who's gonna dance with me
Please stay

I'm never gonna dance again
Guilty feet have got no rhythm
Though it's easy to pretend
I know you're not a fool
Should have known better
Than to cheat a friend
And waste a chance that I've been given
So I'm never gonna dance again
The way I dance with you

Now that you're gone
Was what I did so wrong, so wrong
That you had to leave me all alone?

5 Cowboys And Angels

Words and Music by George Michael

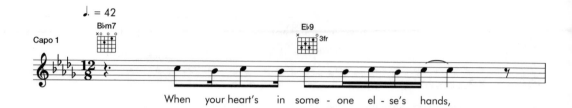

When your heart's in some - one el - se's hands,

mon - key see and mon - key do, their wish is your com - mand,

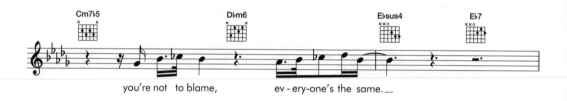

you're not to blame, ev - ery-one's the same. _

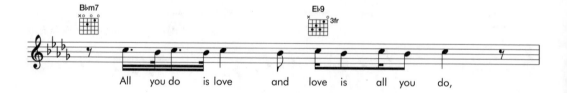

All you do is love and love is all you do,

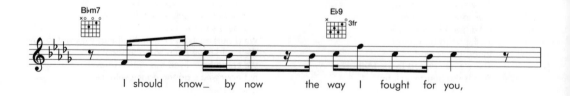

I should know _ by now the way I fought for you,

you're not to blame, ev - ery-one's the same. _ Mmm wo _____

Take this man to your ___ bed, may-be his hands will help you for - get.

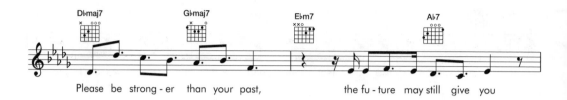

Please be strong - er than your past, the fu - ture may still give you

a chance.

Instrumental
to end

When your heart's in someone else's plans
Things you say and things you do
They don't understand
It's such a shame
Always end the same

You can call it love
But I don't think it's true
You should know by now
I'm not the boy for you
You're not to blame
Always ends the same

I know you think
That you're safe sister
Harmless affection
That keeps things this way
It's the ones who persist
For the sake of a kiss
Who will pay

Cowboys and angels
They all take a shine to you
Why should I imagine
That I was designed for you
Why should I believe
That you would stay

But that scar on your face
That beautiful face of yours
Don't you think that I know
They've hurt you before

Take this man to your bed
Maybe his hands
Will help you forget
Please be stronger than your past
The future may still give you a chance

6 Crazyman Dance

Words and Music by George Michael

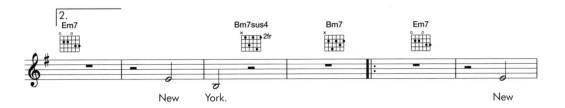

New York. New

York. Just____ like your ma, just____ like your pa, just_

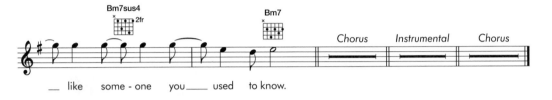

_ like some - one you____ used to know.

Chorus   Instrumental   Chorus

It's been one whole year
And it's just not fair
For all the pushing and shoving
I've still got nothing
I'm never gonna make it
And I'm stuck here in New York
I'm stuck here in New York

So people don't come near
Unless you've a dollar to spare
'Cause you know what they say
About madmen on the subways of New York
(Believe it)

Yesterday's newspapers
I wrap them around my body
Outside these skyscrapers
I wait for the night to hit me
And boy, does it hit me

Instrumental

Just like your ma, just like your pa
Just like someone you used to know

Chorus
Every street and every corner
Watch them drowning
Watch them do the Crazyman Dance
For a nickel or a quarter
For your pleasure
Watch them do the Crazyman Dance

Instrumental

Chorus
I'm coming to London
I'm coming to Paris
I'm gonna make you
Good, clean people embarrassed
Why don't you look at my face
Why don't you look in my eyes
You'd rather look at your feet
You'd rather look at the skies
Oh, you'd look anywhere
But at a man whose pure existence
Says 'I ain't got time'
And I don't care, I don't care
You just don't care, care

7 Desafinado

Words by Newton Ferriera de Mendonca
Music by Antonio Carlos Jobim

Se vo - cê dis-ser__ que eu de-sa - fi - no a-mor,__ yeah,

sai - ba que is-to em mim__ pro - vo - cai - men - sa dôr.__

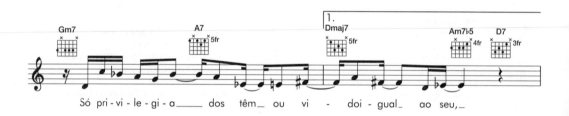

Só pri - vi - le-gi - a____ dos têm__ ou vi - doi-gual__ ao seu,__

e - u pos-su - o a pe - nas o que deus me deu.__

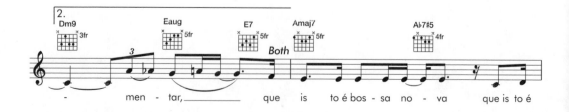

- men - tar,_____ que is to é bos - sa no - va que is to é

mui to na-tu-ral.___ O que vo-ce nao sa - be nem si - quer

___ pre-sen - te,___ é que os de-sa - fi - na dos tam - bem

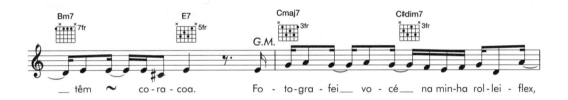

___ têm ~ co-ra-coa. Fo - to-gra-fei___ vo-cé___ na min-ha rol-lei - flex,

___ re-ve - lou-se a su - a e-nor___ mein gra - ti-dão,___ hey.

Só nao___ po-de-ra___ fa-lar as - sim do meu a - mor,_____

ê le é o mai-or___ que vo-cê po - de en - con - trar.___

Vo - cê_ com a su - a mu - si - ca_ es que_ ceu o prin - ci - pal,_ que no

pei-to dos de-sa - fi - na - dos no fun-do do pei - to ba - te ca - la do,_ no

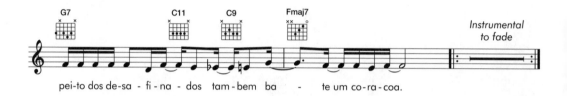

pei-to dos de-sa - fi - na - dos tam-bem ba - te um co-ra-coa.

Instrumental
to fade

Astrud Gilberto
Se você insiste em classificar
O meu comportamento de anti musical
Eu mesmo mentindo possoargumentar
Both
Que is to é bossa nova
Que is to é mui to natural

A.G.
O que você nao sabe nem siquer presente
É que os desafinados tambem têm coracoa
G.M.
Fotografei vocé na minha rolleiflex
Revelouse a sua enor mein gratidão

G.M.
Só nao podera falar assim do meu amor
A.G.
É le é o maior
Both
Que você pode encontrar
Você com a sua musica es que ceu o principal
Que no peito dos desafinados
No fundo do peito bate cala do
No peito dos desafinados tambem bate um coracoa

8 A Different Corner

Words and Music by George Michael

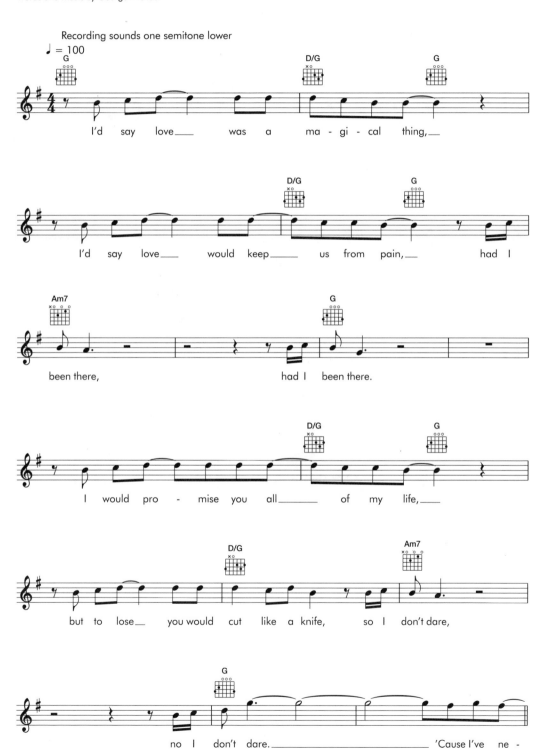

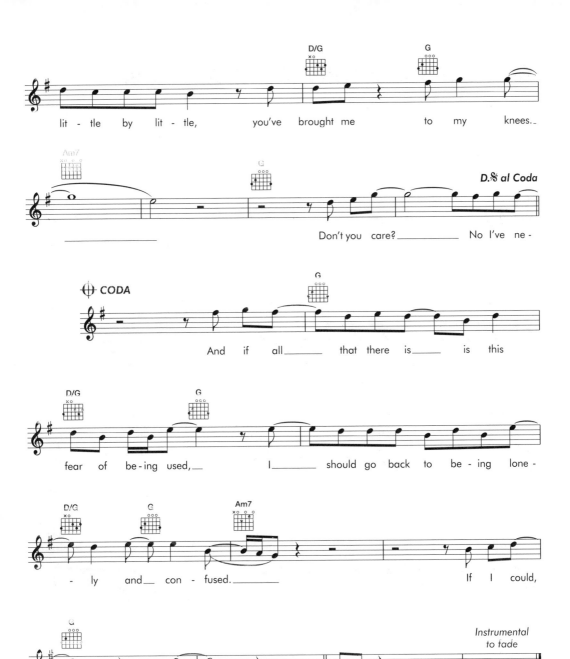

little by little, you've brought me to my knees.

Don't you care?_____ No I've ne-

CODA

And if all_____ that there is_____ is this

fear of be-ing used, __ I_____ should go back to be-ing lone-

- ly and__ con - fused._____ If I could,

I would, __ i swear.

Instrumental to fade

No I've never come close
In all of these years
You are the only one to stop my tears
And I'm so scared of this love

And if all that there is
Is this fear of being used
I should go back to being
Lonely and confused
If I could, I would, I swear

9 Do You Really Want To Know

Words and Music by George Michael

When I ask those ques - tions ba - by, it's

just to get them out of my head. 'Cause they

turn a - round in - side it and they spill

on to our bed. But do I real - ly

want to know? Do I real - ly want to know your life?

Would I have to let you go? Could I lis - ten

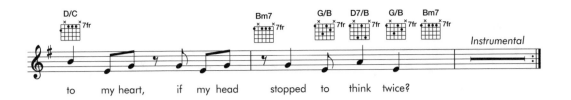

to my heart, if my head stopped to think twice?

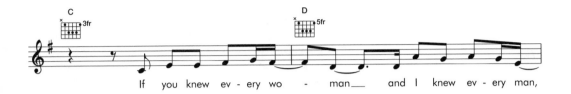

If you knew ev - ery wo - man___ and I knew ev - ery man,

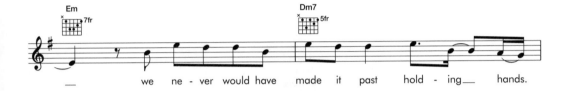

___ we ne - ver would have made it past hold - ing___ hands.

I guess the say - ing is no long - er true,_____ that

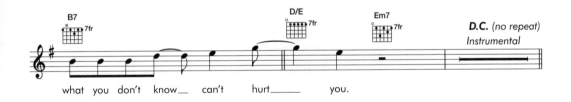

what you don't know___ can't hurt_____ you.

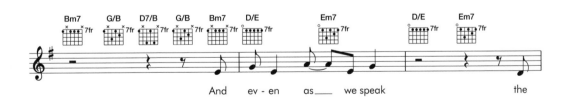

And ev - en as___ we speak the

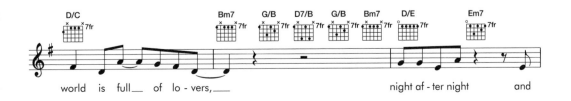

world is full___ of lo - vers,___ night af - ter night and

week   af - ter   week,   trust - ing   to   luck   and   a

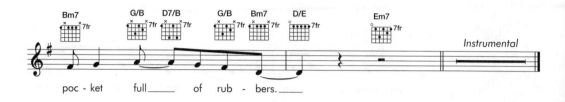

Instrumental

poc - ket   full____   of   rub - bers. ____

Well I've been a good boy
And I've been a bad boy
I have too much fun
But baby so did everyone
I've never been an angel
But things are gonna change, change, change

So do you really want to know?
Do you really want to know my life?
Would you have to let me go?
Could you listen to your heart
If your head stopped to think twice?

If you knew every woman
And I knew every man
We never would have made it past holding hands
I guess the saying is no longer true
That what you don't know can't hurt you

I guess there is just no question baby
You know what you're doing in bed
If I want your touch
Should I know too much
Some things are better left unsaid

So do I really want to know
Do I really want to know your life?
Would I have to let you go?
Could I listen to my heart
If my head starts to think twice?

(Tell me baby, it's one thing to guess, it's one thing to know
And don't you think that maybe baby I've got secrets of my own?)

If you knew every woman
And I knew every man
We never would have made it past holding hands
I used to say it but it's no longer true
'Cause what you don't know can really hurt you
(Can kill you baby)

And even as we speak the world is full of lovers
Night after night, week after week
Trusting to luck and a pocket full of rubbers

10 Don't Let The Sun Go Down On Me

Words and Music by Elton John and Bernie Taupin

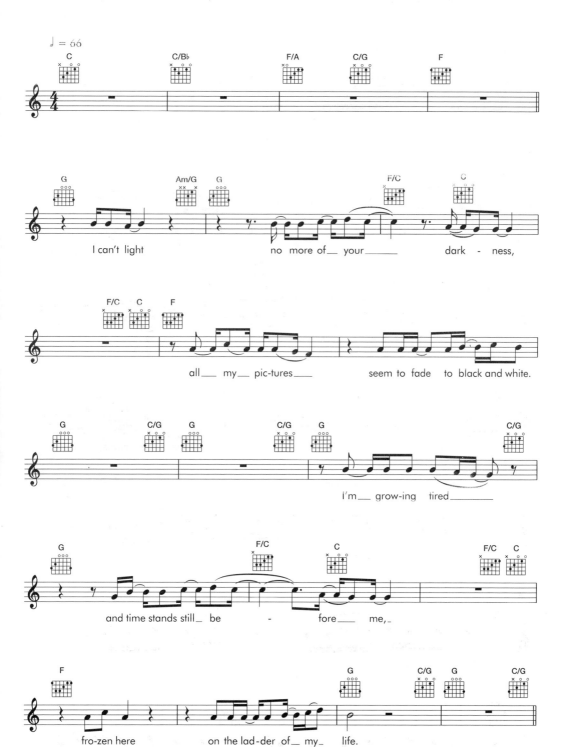

I can't light no more of__ your____ dark - ness,

all__ my__ pic-tures____ seem to fade to black and white.

I'm__ grow-ing tired_____

and time stands still_ be - fore___ me,_

fro-zen here on the lad-der of__ my_ life.

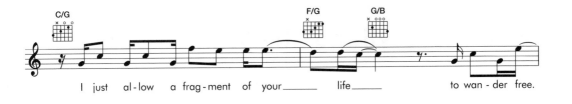

I just al - low a frag - ment of your_____ life_____ to wan - der free.

_____ Oh_____ 'cause los - ing ev - ery - thing__ is like the

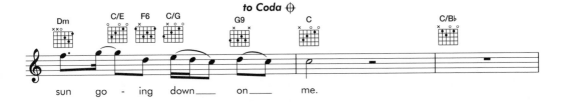

sun go - ing down____ on____ me.

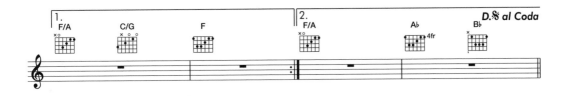

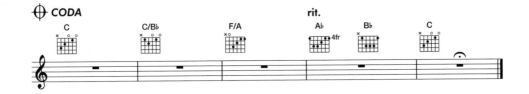

I can't find, oh the right romantic line
But see me once and see the way I feel
Don't discard me just because you think I mean you harm
But these cuts I have, oh they need love to help them heal

Don't let the sun go down on me
Although I search myself, it's always someone else I see
I'd just allow a fragment of your life to wander free
'Cause losing everything is like the sun going down on me

Repeat Chorus

11 Everything She Wants

Words and Music by George Michael

Some - bo - dy told___ me, boy, ev - ery-thing she wants is

ev - ery-thing she sees. I guess I must have loved___ you be-cause I

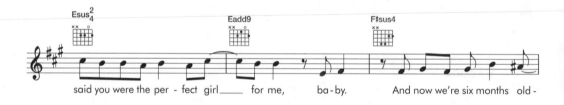

said you were the per - fect girl___ for me, ba - by. And now we're six months old —

— er and ev - ery-thing you want and ev - ery-thing you see

is out of reach, not good e - nough. I don't know what the hell you want

from me.　　Ah ha ha　　Ah ha ha　　Oh ho ho　　Oh ho ho　　Ah ha___

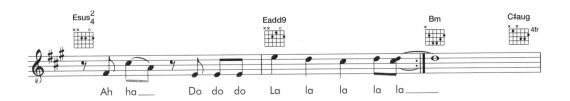

Ah ha___　　Do do do　　La　la　la　la　la___

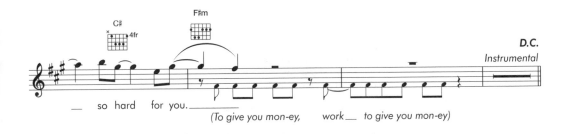

Some - bo - dy　tell___ me___　(Won't you　tell　me)　　why I work

___ so hard　for you.___　(To give you mon-ey,　work___ to give you mon-ey)

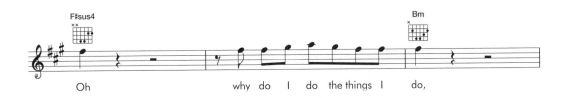

Oh　　　　　why do　I　do the things I　do,

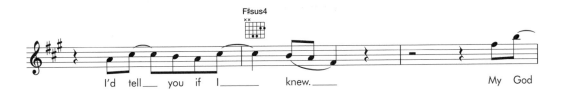

I'd tell___ you if I___　knew.___　　　My God

I don't e-ven think that I love you.

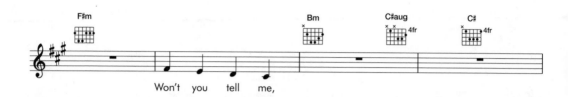

Won't you tell me,

Instrumental with vocal
ad lib. to fade

give you mon-ey, work___ to give you mon-ey.

Some people work for a living
Some people work for fun, girl I just work for you
They told me marriage was give and take
Well you've shown me you can take
You've got some giving to do

And now you tell me that you're having my baby
I'll tell you that I'm happy if you want me to
But one step further and my back will break
If my best isn't good enough
Then how can it be good enough for two
I can't work any harder than I do

Somebody tell me
(Won't you tell me)
Why I work so hard for you
(To give you money, work to give you money)

Oh why do I do the things I do
I'd tell you if I knew
My God I don't even think that I love you

Won't you tell me
Give you money
Work to give you money

12 Faith

Words and Music by George Michael

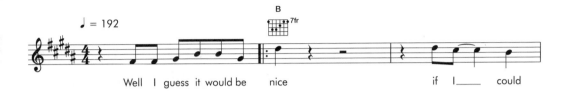

Well I guess it would be nice if I____ could

touch your bo - dy, I know not ev - ery - bo - dy

has got a bo - dy like you.____ But I've got to think

twice, be - fore____ I give my heart____ a - way,

and I know all the games you play be-cause I played them

too.____ Oh but I need some____ time____

_off from___ that e - mo - tion,_____

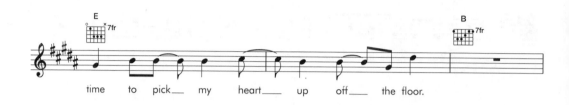

time to pick___ my heart____ up off____ the floor.

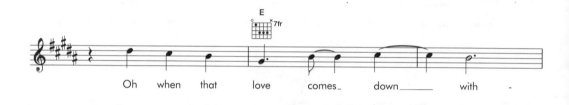

Oh when that love comes_ down_____ with -

- out de - vo - tion, well it takes a strong man ba -

- by, but I'm show-ing you__ the door. Be-cause I've got to have

faith, I've got to have faith,____

be-cause I've got to have   faith,   faith,_   faith,   I've   got to have

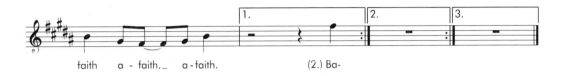

faith   a - faith,_   a - faith.   (2.) Ba-

Baby I know you're asking me to stay
Stay, please, please, please don't go away
You say I'm giving you the blues
Maybe you mean every word you say
Can't help but think of yesterday
And another who tied me down to lover boy rules

Before this river becomes an ocean
Before you throw my heart back on the floor
Oh baby I reconsider my foolish notion
Well I need someone to hold me
But I'll wait for something more

Yes I've got to have faith
I've got to have faith
Because I've got to have faith, faith, faith
I've got to have faith, a-faith, a-faith

Because I've got to have faith
I've got to have faith

Instrumental

Before this river becomes an ocean
Before you throw my heart back on the floor
Oh baby I reconsider my foolish notion
Well I need someone to hold me
But I'll wait for something more

'Cause I gotta have faith
I gotta have faith
'Cause I gotta have faith faith faith
I gotta have faith, a-faith, a-faith

13 Fastlove

Words and Music by George Michael

♩ = 100

Look - ing for___ some e - du - ca - tion, made my way in - to the night.___ All___ that bull - shit con - - ver-sa - tion, ba - by can't you read the signs.___ I won't bore you with the de - tail ba - by, I don't ev - en want to waste your time. Let's_ just say that may - be you could help to ease my mind.___ Ba - - by, I ain't Mis - ter Right, but if you're look-ing for fast_ ___ love, if that's love_ in your_ eyes.___ It's

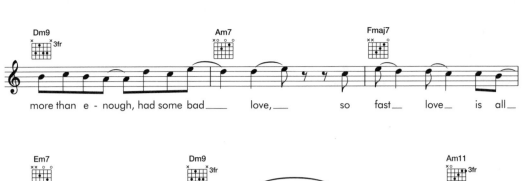

more than e - nough, had some bad____ love, ___ so fast__ love_ is all_

__ that I've_ got on____ my mind._____

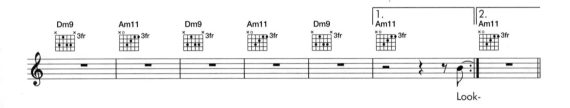

Look-

Got-ta get up__ to get down, you got-ta get up__ to get down. You

got-ta get up__ to get down,_ you got-ta get up__ to get down._ (You)

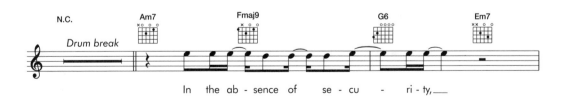

Drum break

In the ab - sence of se - cu - ri - ty, ___

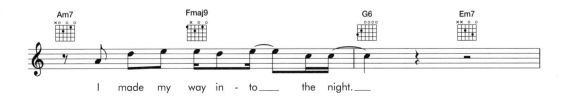

I made my way in - to___ the night.___

Stu - pid Cu - pid keeps on call - ing me, ___

but I see no-thing in ___ his eyes. ___ I miss my ba -

- by, oh yeah! I miss my ba - by, to - night.

_____ So why don't we make ___ a lit - tle room in my B. ___

__ M. W. _____ babe. Search - ing for some peace of mind. __

Hey! ___ I'll help you find it. I do ___ be - lieve ___ that we ___ are prac-

- tic - ing ___ the same ___ re - li - gion. _____

Oh!___ you real-ly ought to get up now.___

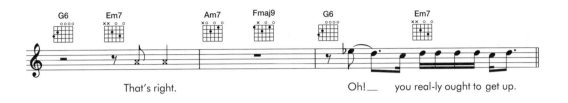

That's right. Oh!___ you real-ly ought to get up.

Got-ta get up__ to get down, you got-ta get up__ to get down. You

play 4 times

got-ta get up__ to get down, you got-ta get up__ to get down. (You)

Looking for some affirmation
Made my way into the sun
My friends got their ladies
They're all having babies
But I just want to have some fun

I won't bore you with the detail baby
Gotta get there in your own sweet time
Lets just say that maybe
You could help me ease my mind

Baby I ain't Mister Right
But if you're looking for fast love
If that's love in your eyes
It's more than enough
Had some bad love
So fast love is all that I've got on my mind

What's there to think about baby?
Get yourself some lessons in love
You gotta get up to get down
You gotta get up to get down
Taste it now baby

In the absence of security
I made my way into the night
Stupid Cupid keeps on calling me
But I see nothing in his eyes

I miss my baby, oh yeah
I miss my baby tonight
So why don't we make a little room
In my B.M.W. babe
Searching for some peace of mind
Hey! I'll help you find it
I do believe that we are
Practicing the same religion
Oh you really ought to get up now
That's right
Oh you really ought to get up

Gotta get up to get down
You gotta get up to get down

14 Fantasy

Words and Music by George Michael

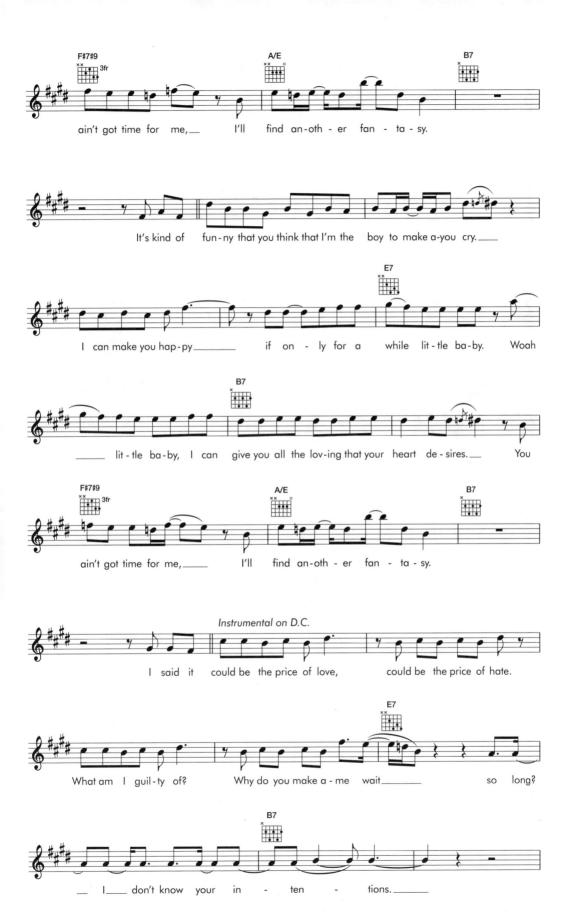

Look to the skies a-bove, I'm in the hands of fate. Push till I get to shove,

E7

I've got to know for hea - ven's sake._____ Is___ this love,

B7   F#7#9

is___ this love or___ in - ven - tion? Ba - by can't you see, I'll

A/E   B7   N.C. **Fine   D.C. al Fine**
                                                          Instrumental

find an-oth - er fan - ta - sy.   Phew!

You hang around with people
Who are sure to make a-you cry
I can make you happy
If only for a while
Little baby, woah little baby
I can give you all the loving
That your heart desires
Give you all the loving
That your heart desires
If only for a while
Little baby, woah little baby
I can give you all the loving
That your heart desires
'Cause if you ain't got time for me
I'll find another fantasy

You take someone's heart
And you kick it around
Keep on picking it up
So you can watch it come down
I don't know what I'm supposed to do
While I wait for you to make up your mind
Could you please be so kind
When you know what to do
I'll be in the next room
But if you leave it too late
I may be in the next state
Hmm

Instrumental

15 Father Figure

Words and Music by George Michael

♩ = 102

Capo 1

B♭sus2 — That's all I want-ed, some-thing spe-cial, some-thing sa-cred, A♭sus2

B♭sus2 — in your__ eyes.__ For just one mo-ment to be bold and

A♭sus2 na-ked B♭sus2 at your__ side.__ G♭sus2 Some-times I think that you ne -

A♭add9 - ver un-der-stand__ me. B♭ G♭sus2 May-be this time is for-ev -

A♭sus2 - er, say it can___ be, Fsus4 wo wo.___ F repeat 1st time only

B♭add9 I will be your fa-ther fi-gure, put your ti-ny hand in mine,

A♭add9 I will be your preach-er teach-er, a-ny-thing you have in mind.

I will be your fa - ther,_____

I will be your preach-er.   Till the end__ of   time.

That's all you wanted
Something special
Someone sacred in your life
Just for one moment
To be warm and naked at my side
Sometimes I think that
You'll never understand me
But something tells me
Together we'd be happy, wo wo

I will be your father figure
Put your tiny hand in mine
I will be your preacher teacher
Anything you have in mind
I will be your father figure
I have had enough of crime
I will be the one who loves you
Till the end of time

Instrumental

That's all I wanted
But sometimes love can be mistaken
For a crime
That's all I wanted
Just to see my baby's
Blue eyes shine

This time I think that
My lover understands me
If we have faith in each other
Then we can be strong baby

I will be your father figure
Put your tiny hand in mine
I will be your preacher teacher
Anything you have in mind

I will be your father figure
I have had enough of crime
I will be the one who loves you
Till the end of time

If you were the desert
I'll be the sea
If you ever hunger
Hunger for me
Whatever you asked for
That's what I'll be

So when you remember
The ones who have lied
Who said that they cared
And then laughed as you cried
Beautiful darling
Don't think of me
Because all I ever wanted
It's in your eyes baby
And love can't lie

Greet me with the eyes of a child
My love is always telling me so
Heaven is a kiss and a smile
Just hold on, hold on
Won't let you go my baby

I will be your father figure
Put your tiny hand in mine
I will be your preacher teacher
Anything you have in mind
I will be your father figure
I have had enough of crime
So I am gonna love you
Till the end of time

16 The First Time Ever I Saw Your Face

Words and Music by Ewan McColl

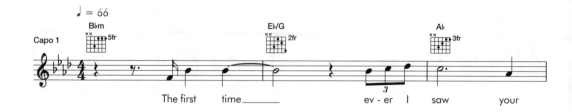

The first time _____ ev - er I saw your

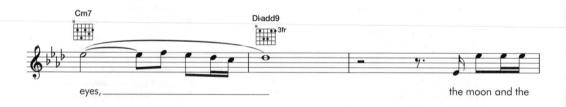

face, I thought the sun _____ rose _ in your

eyes, _____ the moon and the

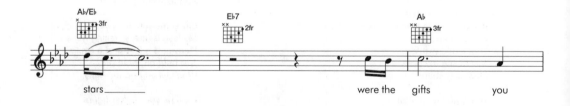

stars _____ were the gifts you

gave to the dark and end - less

skies, my love, to the dark_____

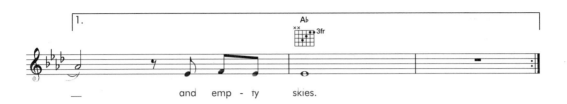

_____ and emp - ty skies.

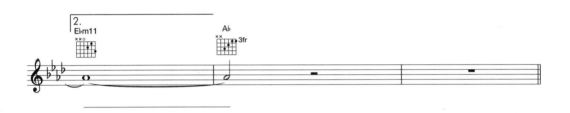

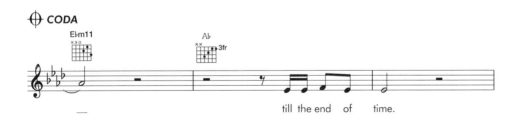

till the end of time.

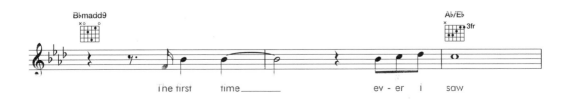

The first time_____ ev - er i saw

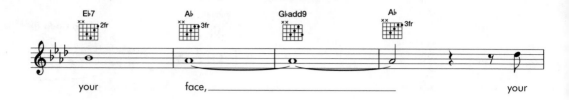

your   face, _____   your

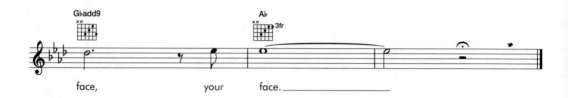

face,   your   face. _____

And the first time ever I kissed your mouth
I felt the earth move in my hands
Like the trembling heart of a captive bird
That was there at my command my love
That was there

And the first time ever I lay with you
And felt your heart so close to mine
And I knew our joy would fill the earth
And would last till the end of time my love
It would last till the end of time

The first time ever I saw your face
Your face, your face

17 Free

Words and Music by George Michael

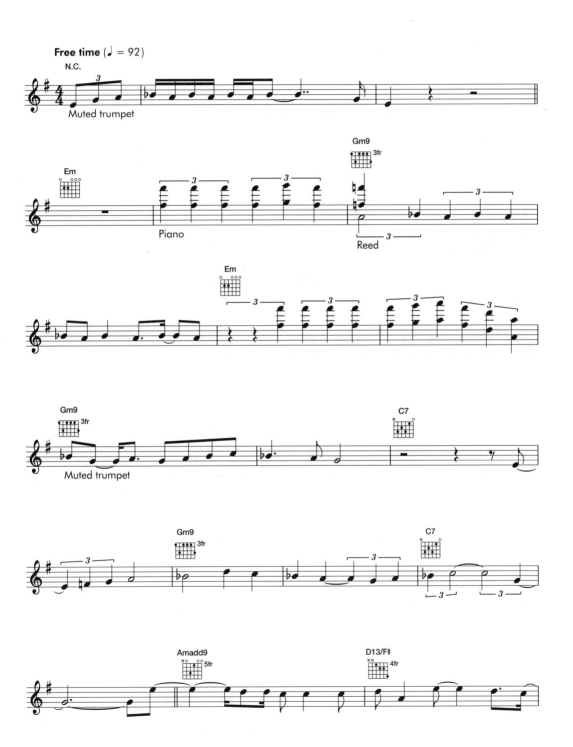

Feels good to be free.

18 Freedom

Words and Music by George Michael

Tell me I'm__ a ba - by__ and I__ don't un - der-stand.

But you know that I'll__ for - give__ you, __ just this

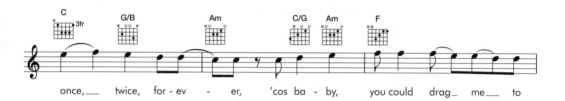

once, __ twice, for - ev - er, 'cos ba - by, you could drag__ me__ to

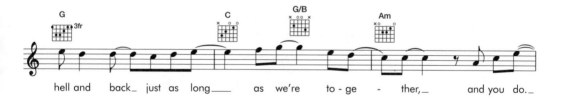

hell and back__ just as long__ as we're to - ge - ther, __ and you do. __

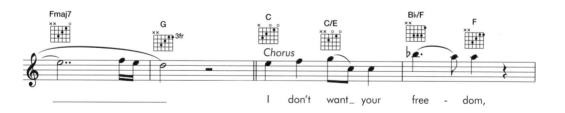

Chorus

I don't want__ your free - dom,

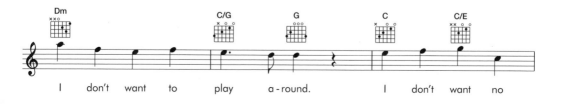

I don't want to play a - round. I don't want no

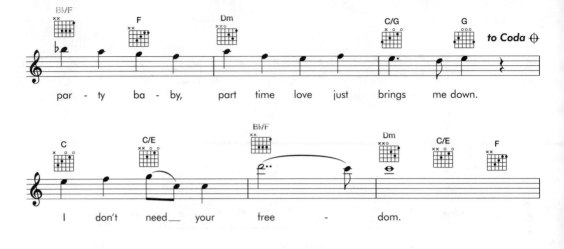

par - ty ba - by, part time love just brings me down.

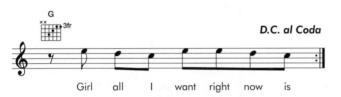 

I don't need__ your free - dom.

Girl all I want right now is

Like a prisoner who has his own key
But I can't escape until you love me
I just go from day to day
Knowing all about the other boys
You take my hand and tell me I'm a fool
To give you all that I do
I bet you some day baby
Someone says the same to you

But you know that I'll forgive you
Just this once twice forever
'Cos baby you could drag me to hell and back
Just as long as we're together
And you do

Chorus
I don't want your freedom
I don't want to play around
I don't want no party baby
Part time love just brings me down
I don't want your freedom
Girl all I want right now is you

Instrumental
You're hurting me baby, hurting me baby
Instrumental
You're hurting me baby, hurting me baby

But you know that I'll forgive you
Just this once twice forever
'Cos baby you could drag me to hell and back
Just as long as we're together
And you do

Chorus ad lib. to fade

19 Freedom '90

Words and Music by George Michael

(yeah) I__ won't let__ you down,__ I will__ not give__ you up,__ got to have some faith__ in the sound,__ it's the one__ good thing that I've got. I__ won't let__ you down,_____ so please don't give__ me up,__ 'cause I__ would real-ly, real-ly love__ to stick a-round. Oh

Instrumental on repeat

Hea-ven knows I was__ just a young boy, did-n't know what I want-ed to be. (did-n't know what I want-ed to be.)__ I was ev-ery lit-tle hun-gry school-girls' pride__ and joy and I guess it was e-nough for me.

Heaven knows we sure had some fun boy
What a kick just a buddy and me
(What a kick just a buddy and me)
We had every big shot good time band on the run boy
We were living in a fantasy
(We were living in a fantasy)
We won the race, got outta the place
Went back home, got a brand new face
For the boys at M.T.V.
But today the way I play the game
Has got to change
Oh yeah
Now I'm gonna get me some happy

I think there's something you should know
I think it's time I stopped the show
There's something deep inside of me
There's someone I forgot to be
Take back your picture in the frame
Don't think that I'll be back again
Just hope you'll understand
Sometimes the clothes do not make the man

All we have to do now
Is to take these lies
And make them true
(Somehow)
All we have to see
Is that I don't belong to you
And you don't belong to me

(Freedom)
I won't let you down
(Freedom)
I will not give you up
(Freedom)
You've got to live for what you take
Got to have some faith in the sound
It's the one good thing that I've got
Freedom
I won't let you down
Freedom
So please don't give me up
Freedom
'Cause I would really, really love to stick around

Well it looks like the road to heaven
But it feels like the road to hell
But I know which side my bread was buttered
I took the knife as well
Posing for another picture
Everybody's got to sell
But when you shake your ass they notice fast
Some mistakes were built to last

That's what you get
(That's what you get)
That's what you get
(I say that's what you get)
I say that's what you get
For changing your mind
That's what you get
For changing your mind
And after all this time
I just hope you'll understand
Sometimes the clothes do not make the man

Chorus ad lib.

20 Hand To Mouth

Words and Music by George Michael

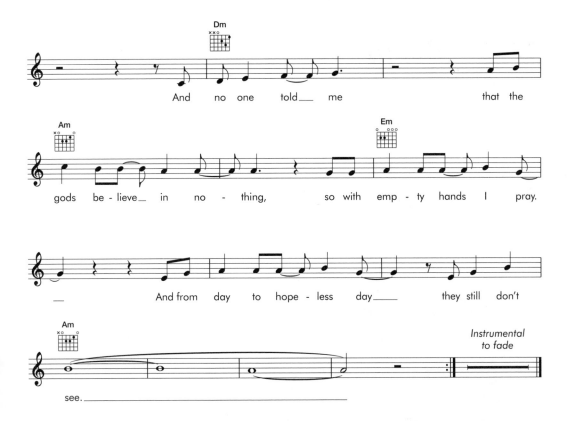

Dm

And no one told___ me that the

Am **Em**

gods be - lieve___ in no - thing, so with emp - ty hands I pray.

___ And from day to hope - less day___ they still don't

Am

Instrumental to fade

see. ___

Sweet little baby on a big white doorstep
She needs her mother but her mother is dead
Just another hooker that the lucky can forget
Just another hooker it happens every day
She left a little baby
But she couldn't bear to see him living
Hand to mouth, hand to mouth
Hand to mouth, hand to mouth

I believe in the gods of America
I believe in the land of the Free
And no-one told me
That the gods believe in nothing
So with empty hands I pray
And from day to hopeless day
They still don't see

Everybody talks about the new generation
Jump on the wagon or they'll leave you behind
But no-one gave a thought to the rest of the nation
I'd like to help you buddy, but I haven't got the time
Somebody shouted save me
But everybody started living
Hand to mouth, hand to mouth
Hand to mouth, hand to mouth

There's a big white lady on a big white doorstep
She asked her daddy and her daddy said yes
Has to give a little for the dollars that we get
Has to give a little, they say it's for the best
Somebody shouted maybe
But they kept on living from
Hand to mouth, hand to mouth
Hand to mouth, hand to mouth

So she went to the arms of America
(America, America)
And she kissed the powers that be
And someone told me, someone told me
That the gods believe in nothing
So with empty hands I pray
And I tell myself one day
It just might stop
You just might see

21 Happy

Words and Music by George Michael

_ yeah. I_____ can make you hap - py yeah,_

_ yeah, don't ya, don't ya know that I_____ can make you hap - py.

D.C. _no repeat_   _repeat Chorus ad lib._
Instrumental

Boys   and

Boys and girls
The ones who kiss and tell
Why should we have to believe them?
No, I don't understand
How any woman, how any man
Can say 'Lay me down, lay me down'
For that big-stash, cheap-cash
Think-about-the-money

Chorus
I can make you happy (yeah, yeah)
Don't you know that?
I can make you happy (yeah, yeah)
I can make you happy (yeah, yeah)
Don't you know that
'I can make you happy'
And these things that keep you happy honey

Instrumental

I've seen you in the corner
With your rub-it-on tan
Hitching a ride
Could be a woman or a man
Gonna get what you want before too long
Gonna take your opportunities
Right or wrong
Some poor cow with a seven-year itch?
You don't dig men
But you'll fuck 'em if they're rich
You can't be with me
You're a lowlife daughter
Of a son of a bitch

Chorus ad lib to end

22 Hard Day

Words and Music by George Michael

Recording sounds one semitone lower

♩ = 100

(down.) Don't bring me down.

I've ne-ver been one for play-ing games, you can

move your mouth for-ev - er___ but the words sound just the same, some-thing like

bang bang, you're dead. Can we just make love___ in - stead, ___

say yes, 'cause it's what we do best, I've had such a hard day.

Take me where their eyes can't find us, with - out___ you___ I may as well just . . .

Instrumental on repeat

How much do___ I have to say, what more do___ you have to see,

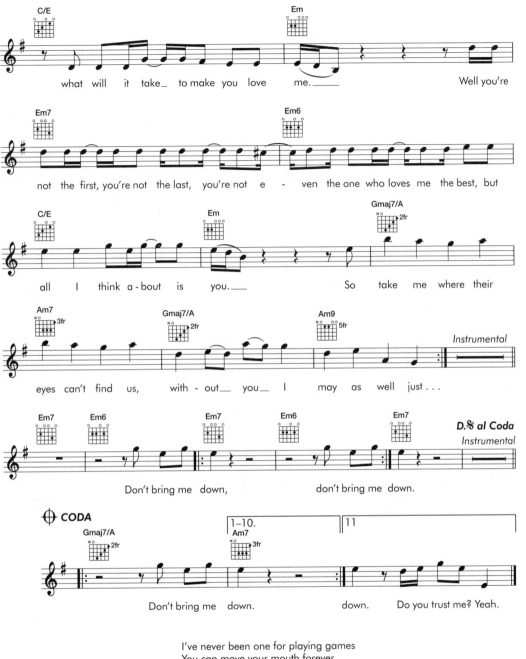

what will it take_ to make you love me._ Well you're

not the first, you're not the last, you're not e - ven the one who loves me the best, but

all I think a-bout is you._ So take me where their

eyes can't find us, with - out_ you_ I may as well just . . .

Instrumental

Don't bring me down, don't bring me down.

D.%. al Coda
Instrumental

CODA

1–10.

11

Don't bring me down. down. Do you trust me? Yeah.

I've never been one for playing games
You can move your mouth forever
But the words sound just the same
Bang bang, you're dead
Shouldn't we just make love instead
Say yes 'cause it's what we do best
I've had such a hard day

Don't bring me down
Won't you give me a break

Sweet little boy with oh such a big mouth
Harsh words can get you into hot water
When people don't understand you baby
I'm always here for you
And I, and I will never bring you down baby
Trust me, I want you to trust me
'Cause I won't bring you down
Do you trust me?
Yeah!

23 Heal The Pain

Words and Music by George Michael

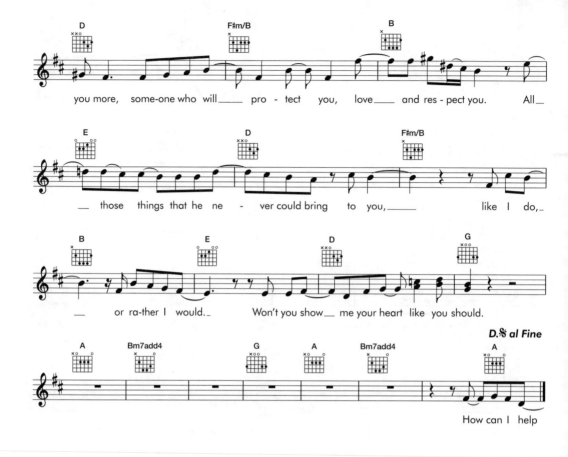

you more, some-one who will____ pro - tect you, love____ and res - pect you. All_

____ those things that he ne - ver could bring to you,____ like I do,_

_ or ra-ther I would._ Won't you show__ me your heart like you should.

D.%̸ al Fine

How can I help

He must have really hurt you
To make you say the things that you do
He must have really hurt you
To make those pretty eyes look so blue
He must have known that he could
That you'd never leave him
Now you can't see my love is good
And that I'm not him

Chorus
How can I help you?
Please let me try to
I can heal the pain
Won't you let me inside
Whenever you want me
You know that I will be
Waiting for the day
That you'll say you'll be mine

Won't you let me
Let this love begin
Won't you show me your heart now
I'll be good to you
I can make this thing true
Show me that heart right now

Who needs a lover that can't be a friend?
Something tells me I'm the one
You've been looking for
If you ever should see him again
Won't you tell him
You've found someone who gives you more
Someone who will protect you
Love and respect you
All those things that he never could
Bring to you like I do
Or rather I would
Won't you show me your heart
Like you should

Instrumental

How can I help you?
Please let me try to
I can heal the pain
That you're feeling inside
Whenever you want me
You know that I will be
Waiting for the day
That you say you'll be mine

Won't you let me in
Let this love begin
Won't you show me your heart now
I'll be good to you
I can make this thing true
And get to your heart somehow

24 I Believe (When I Fall In Love It Will Be Forever)

Words and Music by Stevie Wonder and Yvonne Wright

♩ = 132

Shat - tered dreams, __ worth - less years, __ here am __ I __ en - cased in - side __ a hol - low shell. __

Life be - gan, __ then was done, __ now I __ stare __ in - to __ a cold __ and emp - ty well. __

Ma - ny sounds that greet our ears, the sights our eyes __ be - hold __ will op - en up our merg - ing hearts and feed our emp - ty souls. __

- swered my_____ prayers,__ won't you lis - ten to him now.

Oh c-'mon let's fall in love. You're the one that I've been wait-

- ing for,_____ c-'mon let's fall in love.

You're the wo-man that I a - dore._____ Don't you wan-na, don't you

repeat ad lib. to fade

wan-na, don't you wan-na fall in love with me ba - by. No a

Without despair, we will share
And the joys of caring will not be erased
What has been, must never end
The joys of caring will not be replaced

When the seeds of love are planted firm
They won't be hard to find
And the songs of love I sing to you
Will echo in my mind
Hey!

Chorus
I believe when I fall in love with you
It will be forever
I believe when I fall in love this time
It will be forever

You know God has answered my prayers
Won't you listen to him now
God sure answered my prayers
Won't you listen to him now
God will answer your prayers
Just ask him and God sure
Will answer all your prayers

Oh come on, let's fall in love
You're the one that I've been waiting for
Come on, let's fall in love
You're the woman that I adore
Don't you wanna, don't you wanna
Don't you wanna fall in love with me baby

Ad lib. to fade

25 I Can't Make You Love Me

Words and Music by Mike Reid and Allen Shamblin

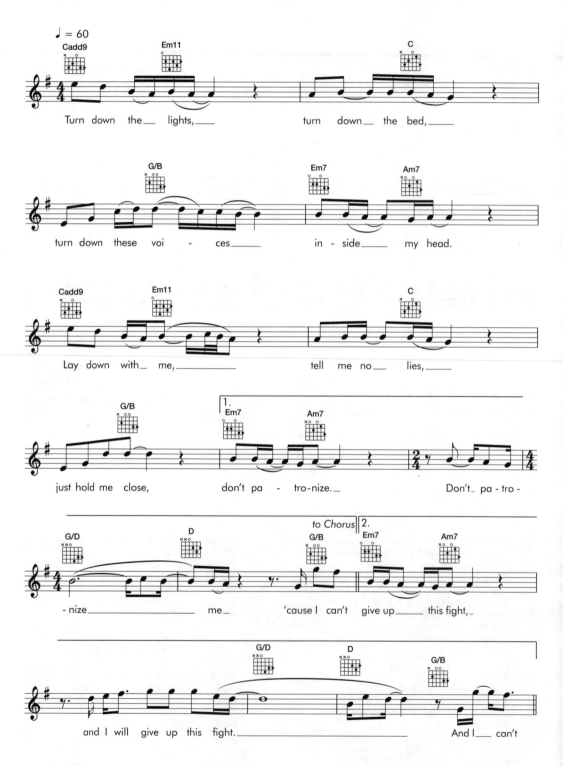

s'no good for me ba - by   with-out   love.

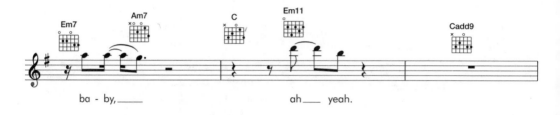

_____   All my tears, all these years, ev-ery place   I be-lieved   in

ba - by,_____   ah___ yeah.

rit.

Some-one's gon-na love me.

I close my eyes
Then I won't see
The love you do not feel
When you're holding me
Mornin' will come
And I'll do what's right
Just give me till then
To give up this fight
And I will give up this fight

And I can't make you love me
If you don't
You can't make your heart
Feel something that it won't
And here in the dark
In these final hours
I will lay down my heart
And I'll feel the power
But you won't, no you won't

And I can't make you love me
If you don't
Ain't no use in you trying
S'no good for me baby without love
All my tears, all these years
Every place I believed in baby, ah yeah

Someone's gonna love me

26 I Knew You Were Waiting (For Me)

Words and Music by Dennis Morgan and Simon Climie

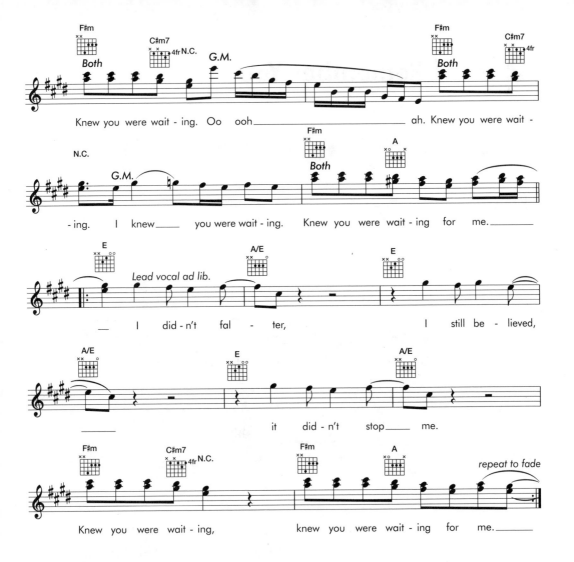

A.F.
With an endless desire, I kept on searching
Sure in time our eyes would meet
Like the bridge is on fire, the hurt is over
One touch and you set me free
G.M.
No I don't regret a single moment, no I don't
A.F.
I know you don't
G.M.
Looking back
When I think of all those diappointments
I just laugh
A.F.
I know you do
G.M.
I just laugh

Both
When the river was deep
I didn't falter
When the mountain was high
I still believed
When the valley was low
It didn't stop me, no no
I knew you were waiting
I knew you were waiting for me

A.F.
So we were drawn together through destiny
I know this love we shared
Was meant to be
Both
Knew you were waiting
Knew you were waiting
G.M.
I knew you were waiting
Both
Knew you were waiting for me

I didn't falter
I still believed
It didn't stop me
Knew you were waiting
Knew you were waiting for me
I didn't falter
I still believed
It didn't stop me
Knew you were waiting
Knew you were waiting for me

Lead vocal ad lib.

27 I Remember You

Words by Johnny Mercer
Music by Victor Schertzinger

Freely (♩ = c.45)

Capo 1

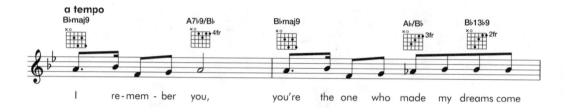

a tempo

I re-mem-ber you, you're the one who made my dreams come

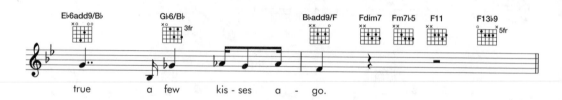

true a few kis-ses a - go.

I re-mem-ber you, you're the one who said I love you

too. Did - n't you know?

I re-mem-ber too, a dis - tant bell and stars that

28 I Want Your Sex
(Part I 'Lust')

Words and Music by George Michael

There's things that you guess and things that you know. There's
boys you can trust and girls that you don't. There's lit-tle things you hide and
lit-tle things that you show. Some-times you think you're gon-na get it, but you
don't and that's just the way it goes. I swear I won't tease you, won't
tell you no lies. I don't need no Bi-ble just look in my eyes. I've
wait-ed so long ba-by, now that we're friends, ev-ery
man's got his pa-tience and here's where mine ends. I want your

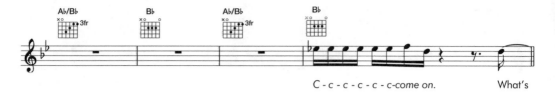

C - c - c - c - c - c-come on.   What's

_ your de-fi-ni-tion of dir - ty ba - by? What_ do you con-si-der porn - o - gra-phy?   Don't

_ you know I love you till it hurts me ba - by? Don't you think it's time you had sex with me?   What's

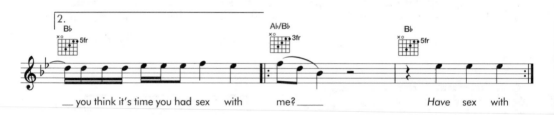

_ you think it's time you had sex   with   me?_____   Have   sex   with

me._____   C - c - c - c - c - c-come on._

It's playing on my mind
It's dancing on my soul
It's taken so much time
So why don't you just let me go?
I'd really like to try
Oh I'd really love to know
When you tell me you're gonna regret it
Then I tell you that I love you
But you still say no

i swear i won't tease you
Won't tell you no lies
I don't need no Bible
Just look in my eyes
I've waited so long baby
Out in the cold
But I can't take much more girl
I'm losing control

I want your sex, I want your love
I want your sex, I want your sex

It's natural, it's chemical
It's logical, habitual
It's sensual but most of all
Sex is something we should do
Sex is something for me and you
Sex is natural, sex is good
Not everybody does it
But everybody should
Sex is natural, sex is fun
Sex is best when it's one on one

I'm not your father, I'm not your brother
Talk to your sister, I am a lover
What's your definition of dirty baby?
What do you consider pornography?
Don't you know I love you
Till it hurts me baby?
Don't you think it's time
You had sex with me?
Have sex with me
Come on

29 I Want Your Sex (Part II)

Words and Music by George Michael

C - c-c-c-c-c-c-c-c-c-come on.___ D-n-d-d-n-d-n-d-d - do do.

D-d-d-d-n-d-n-d-d - do do. Oh___ yeah.___

I, I, I want you ba - by.___ Oh

I want you ba - by.___

Oh___ so much love___ that___ you've___ ne -

- ver seen. Let's make love, ___ put your___ trust

in me. Mm,___ don't you lis - ten to what they

30 I Want Your Sex (Part III 'A Last Request')

Words and Music by George Michael

It's late,___ time_____ for___ bed.

So I sit and I wait___ for that gin and to-nic to

go to your head.___ I know___

it's a de-vi-ous plan,___ but it's the on-ly___ way that I know

___ to get those big, bad car keys out of your hand.

You know___ that I re-main a gen-tle-man,

but ev-en so___ there's on-ly so___ much a gen-tle-man can stand.

Sleep with me
Oh sleep with me tonight

Instrumental

My cards are on the table
My dreams are in your bed
Oh, if I was able
I'd be there instead

Oh sleep with me tonight

Instrumental

31   I'm Your Man

Words and Music by George Michael

Call me good,___ call me bad,___ call me

a-ny-thing you want to ba - by. But I know___ that you're sad

___ and I know___ I'll make you hap-py with the one thing that you ne-ver had.

Ba - by,___ I'm your man.___ Don't__ you know that__

ba - by,___ I'm your___ man.___ You bet!

If you're gon-na do it, do it right, right? Do it with me. If you're gon-na do it, do it

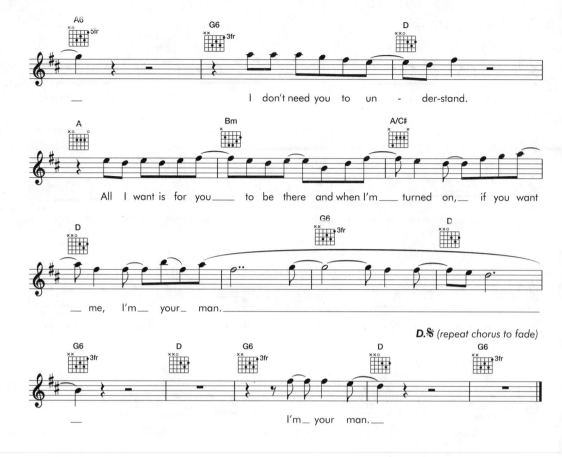

I don't need you to un - der-stand.

All I want is for you___ to be there and when I'm___ turned on,___ if you want

___ me, I'm___ your_ man._____

D.% *(repeat chorus to fade)*

___ I'm_ your man. ___

You're so good, you're divine
Wanna take you, wanna make you
But they tell me it's a crime
Everybody knows
Where the good people go
But where we're going baby
Ain't no such word as no
Baby I'm your man
Don't you know who I am?
Baby I'm your man
You bet!

If you gonna do it
Do it right, right?
Do it with me
If you're gonna do it
Do it right, right?
Do it with me

To do it on my own first class information
I'll be your sexual inspiration
And with some stimulation
We can do it right

Instrumental

So why waste time with the other guys
When you can have mine
I ain't asking for no sacrifice
Baby your friends do not need to know
I've got a real nice place to go *(Listen!)*
I don't need you to care
I don't need you to understand
All I want is for you to be there
And when I'm turned on
If you want me
I'm your man

If you're gonna do it
Do it right, right?
Do it with me
If you're gonna do it
Do it right, right?
Do it with me
If you're gonna do it
You know what I say
If you're gonna do it
Don't throw it away
Don't throw it baby

Because
I'll be your boy, I'll be your man
I'll be the one who understands
I'll be your first, I'll be your last
I'll be the only one you ask
I'll be your friend, I'll be your toy
I'll be the one who brings you joy
I'll be your hope, I'll be your pearl
I'll take you half way round the world!
I'll make you rich, I'll make your poor
Just don't use the door
Do it with me

32   If You Were My Woman

Words and Music by Clare McMurray, Pamela Sawyer and Leon Ware

wo-man,   here's what I would do, oh,_____   I'd

ne - ver, no,__   no, no,   stop lov - ing_____

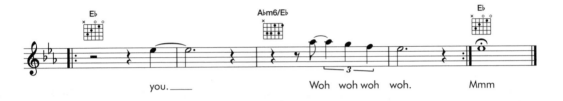

you._____   Woh woh woh woh.   Mmm

He tears you down darlin'	If you were my woman
Says you're nothing at all	If you were my woman
But I'll be there for you darlin'	If you were my woman
When he lets you fall	Here's what I would do, oh
You're like a diamond	I'd never, no, no, no
But he treats you like glass	Stop lovin' you
Yet you beg him to love you	Woh! Oh! My darlin'
With me you don't ask	
	If you were my woman
If you were my woman	Sweet lovin' woman
If you were my woman	I said
If you were my woman	If you were my woman
Here's what I'd do, oh	Here's what I would do, oh
I'd never, no, no, no	I'd never, no, no, no
Stop lovin' you	Stop lovin' you
Woh! Yeah! My darlin'	Woh! Yeah!
	Never, never, no
Life is so crazy	
And love is so unkind	
Because he came first darlin'	
Will he hang on your mind	
You're a part of me	
And you don't even know it	
I'm what you need	
But I'm too afraid to show it	

33   It Doesn't Really Matter

Words and Music by George Michael

♩ = 60 (Swing 16ths)

It does-n't real - ly mat - ter that__ I love__

__ you.   How ma-ny rea - sons call?__   It does-n't real-ly mat-ter at all.__

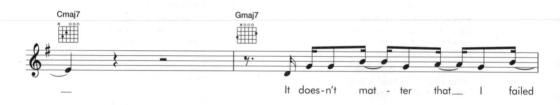

It does-n't mat - ter that__ I failed

__ to break down your fa-ther's wall.__   It real-ly does-n't mat-ter at all.__

Why_____   tell me you__ don't un - der - stand when you do?

I thought I had some-thing to say,____ but it real-ly does-n't mat-ter at all,

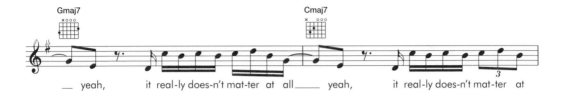

__ yeah, it real-ly does-n't mat-ter at all____ yeah, it real-ly does-n't mat-ter at

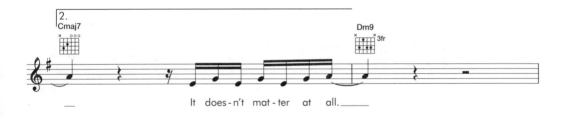

all yeah, it real-ly does-n't mat-ter._____ I changed my name

__ It does-n't mat-ter at all.____

Lov-ing you less, pro-mis-es, pro-mis-es.____

And it's no good look-ing back, be-cause time's

_____ a thief, and I_____ be-lieve_ that I'm too old_ for that._ We're just

say-ing the things_____ that we_ have said_ for-ev - er.

It

does-n't real - ly mat - ter that_ I love_____ you. How ma-ny sea - sons_____

_____ fall? It's too bad,_____ it real-ly does-n't mat-ter at

all yeah, it real-ly does-n't mat-ter at all_____ yeah, it real-ly does-n't mat-ter at all_

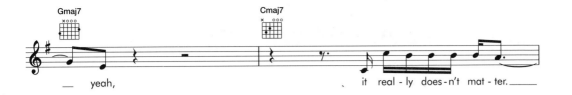

yeah,

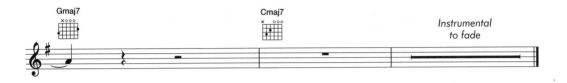

it real - ly does - n't mat - ter.____

Gmaj7   Cmaj7   Instrumental
                  to fade

____

I changed my name
To be rid of the things that I want from you
It's strange
But a name is a name
And the truth is the truth

Oh there is always
Always someone there to remind me
So I learned to live with shame
Tell myself I feel no pain
But I do
And if I have to tell you
Then it really doesn't matter at all yeah
It really doesn't matter at all
It really doesn't matter at all yeah
It really doesn't matter
It doesn't matter at all

Loving you less, promises, promises
And it's no good looking back
Because time is a thief
And I believe that I'm too old for that
We're just saying the things
That we have said forever

It doesn't really matter that I love you
How many seasons fall?
It's too bad
It really doesn't matter at all yeah
It really doesn't matter at all yeah
It really doesn't matter at all yeah
It really doesn't matter

34　It's Alright With Me

Words and Music by Cole Porter

35 Jesus To A Child

Words and Music by George Michael

Sadness in my eyes
No-one guessed
Well no-one tried
You smiled at me
Like Jesus to a child

Loveless and cold
With your last breath
You saved my soul
You smiled at me
Like Jesus to a child

And what have I learned
From all these tears?
I've waited for you
All those years
But just when it began
He took your love away

But I still say
When you find love
When you know that it exists
Then the lover that you miss
Will come to you
On those cold nights, cold nights

When you've been loved
When you know it holds such bliss
Then the lover that you kissed
Will comfort you
When there's no hope in sight

So the words you could not say
I'll sing them for you
And the love we would have made
I'll make it for two
For every single memory
Has become a part of me
You will always be my love

Well I've been loved
So I know just what love is
And the lover that I kissed
Is always by my side
Oh the lover I still miss
Was Jesus to a child

36 Killer/Papa Was A Rolling Stone

Words and Music by
Sealhenri Samuel and Adam Tinley

Words and Music by
Norman Whitfield and Barrett Strong

37 Kissing A Fool

Words and Music by George Michael

You are far
I'm never gonna be your star
I'll pick up the pieces and mend my heart
Maybe I'll be strong enough
I don't know where to start
But I'll never find peace of mind
While I listen to my heart

People, you can never change the way they feel
Better let them do just what they will
For they will
If you let them steal your heart
People, will always make a lover feel a fool
But you knew I loved you
We could have shown them all

But remember this
Every other kiss that you ever give
Long as we both live
When you need the hand of another man
One you really can surrender with
I will wait for you like I always do
There's something there
That can't compare with any other

You are far
When I could have been your star
You listened to people
Who scared you to death and from my heart
Strange that I was wrong enough
To think you'd love me too
Guess you were kissing a fool
You must have been kissing a fool

38 Look At Your Hands

Words and Music by George Michael and David Austin

Bet-cha don't, bet-cha don't, bet-cha don't like___ it. Na na na na na na la - dy

look at your hands, you've got two fat chil-dren and a drunk - en___ man.

And I bet_____ you don't like___ your life___

repeat to fade

now._____

Ma ma ma ma ma ma baby
Look at your hands
You should have been my woman
When you had the chance
Betcha don't, betcha don't
Betcha don't like your life
Betcha don't, betcha don't
Betcha don't like your life now

He hits you once, he hits you twice
He don't care about the blood on his hands
But that's ok 'cause it's his wife
It's the only thing she understands
He says
Say you're gonna leave him
Say you're gonna try
But you're only talking
Oh I know you think I'm a young boy
But I'm good and I think we can make it

Chorus

Well excuse me baby
But it's making me mad
The only one you wanted
Is the only one you'll never have
Betcha don't, betcha don't
Betcha don't like your life
Betcha don't, betcha don't
Betcha don't like it

Na na na na na na na lady
Look at your hands
You've got two fat children
And a drunken man
And I bet you don't like your life now

39 Miss Sarajevo

Words and Music by Brian Eno, Bono, The Edge, Adam Clayton and Larry Mullen Jnr

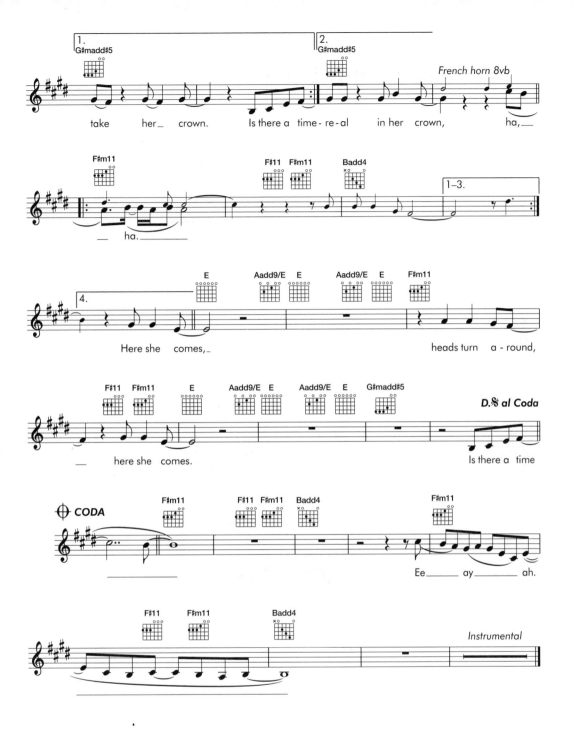

Is there a time to run for cover
A time for kiss and tell?
Is there a time for different colours
Different names you find it hard to spell?

Is there a time for first communion
A time for East Seventeen?
Is there a time to turn to Mecca
Is there time to be a beauty queen?

Here she comes, heads turn around
Here she comes, surreal in her crown, ha ha

Here she comes, heads turn around
Here she comes

Is there a time for tying ribbons
A time for Christmas trees?
Is there a time for laying tables
And the night is set to freeze?

40 A Moment With You

Words and Music by George Michael

You can't_ keep a-hold-ing it in_ when it's some-

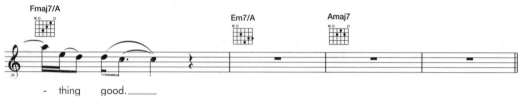

- thing good._____

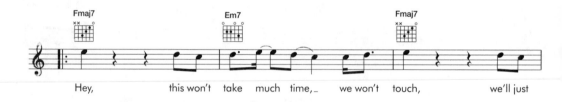

Hey,   this won't take much time,_ we won't touch,   we'll just

wait   for__ signs._   And_   no - thing__ was   fur - ther from my   mind,

_   than this   mo-ment with   you.____   Woh____

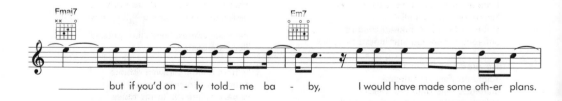

_____ but if you'd on - ly told_ me ba - by,   I would have made some oth-er plans.

If I'd on - ly seen it soon - er,___ but what a way with_ your hands

you ___ had. I want-ed that_ mo - ment with you. _____

I know that it's wrong, 'If you need me, I'm_ here' _____ turns me

on. _____ I can't help think-ing it's a mi - ra - cle _____

_ you're here. I can't help think-ing it's a mi-ra-cle. __

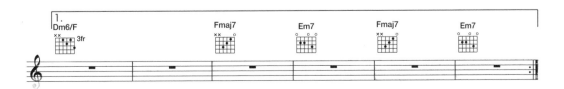

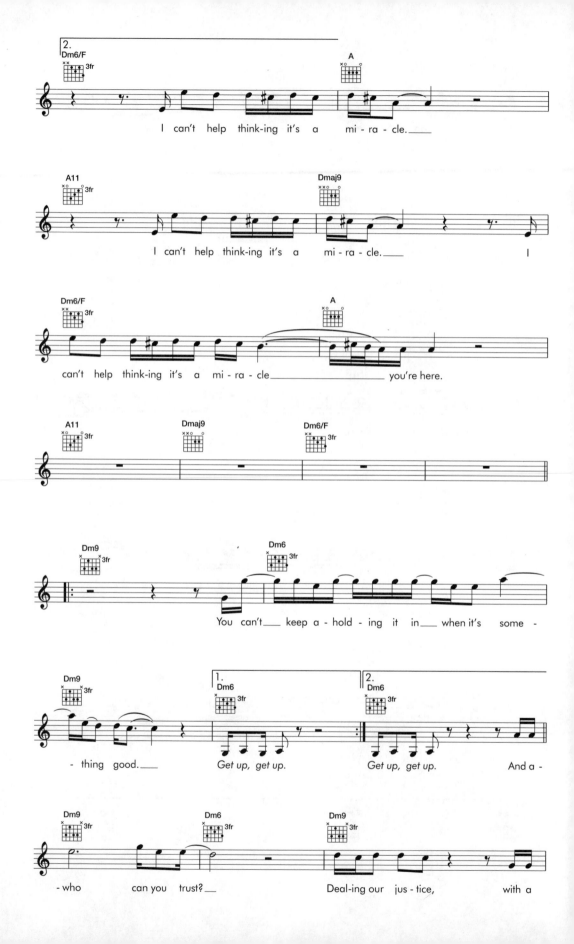

mi-ni - mum of fuss.   Who_____ ba - by?

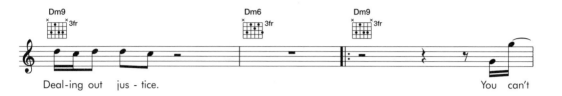

Deal-ing out jus - tice.   You can't

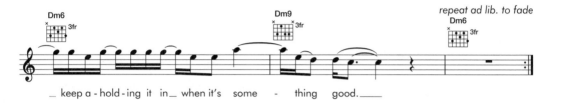

_ keep a - hold-ing it in_ when it's some - thing good.____

Say, you don't waste much time
We don't touch do we baby
But still my hands are tied
For that moment with you

Woh, but if you'd only told me baby
I would have made some other plans
If I'd only seen it sooner
But what a way with your hands you had
I wanted that moment with you

You know that I'm strong
I've no reason to fear
Or am I wrong?
I can't help thinking it's a miracle you're here
I can't help thinking it's a miracle

I can't help thinking it's a miracle
I can't help thinking it's a miracle you're here

You can't keep a-holding it in
when it's something good
Get up, get up
Get up, get up
And a-who can you trust?
Dealing out justice
With a minimum of fuss
Who baby?
Dealing out justice
You can't keep a-holding it in
When it's something good

41 Monkey

Words and Music by George Michael

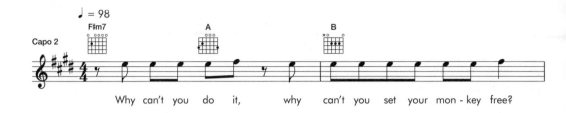

Why can't you do it, why can't you set your mon - key free?

Al - ways giv - ing in to it, do you love the mon - key or do__ you love me?

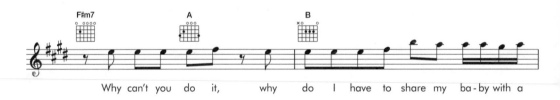

Why can't you do it, why do I have to share my ba - by with a

mon - key, with a mon - key? Oh I

count to ten but I don't know how and I don't know when to o -

- pen my eyes. If you kiss me a - gain like you

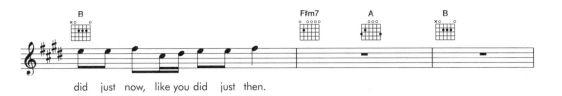

did just now, like you did just then.

I've had the rest, now it's time I had the best,_ so you

tell me that_ you won't do a - ny - more._____ Well I'd

write your heart a let - ter, but I think you know me bet - ter. If I

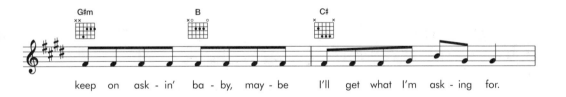

keep on ask - in' ba - by, may - be I'll get what I'm ask - ing for.

Why can't you do it, why can't you set your mon - key free?

Al - ways giv - ing in to it, do you love the mon - key, or do_ you love me?

Why can't you do it,   why   do   I   have   to   share   my   ba - by   with   a

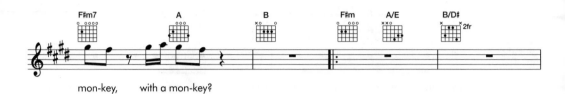

mon-key,   with a mon-key?

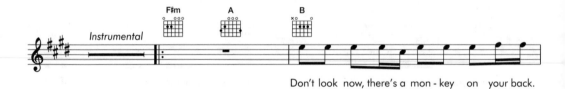

Oh   I

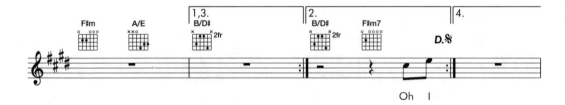

Don't look now, there's a mon - key   on   your back.

Don't look now, there's a mon - key on __ your . . .

So you   tell   me that __ you   won't   do   a   -   ny - more,

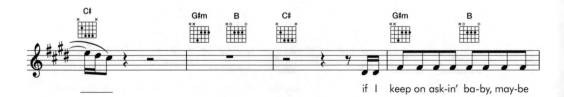

if I   keep on ask-in' ba-by, may-be

Oh I hate your friends
But I don't know how and I don't know when
To open your eyes
Yes your monkey's back again
Do you want him now like you did back then?

I tried my best
But your head is such a mess
So I guess that I don't want you anymore
Well you say you care about me
That you just can't do without me
But you keep on dancing baby
Till that monkey has you on the floor

Why can't you do it
Why can't you set your monkey free?
Always giving in to it
Do you love the monkey
Or do you love me?
Why can't you do it
Why do I have to share my baby
With a monkey, with a monkey?

Instrumental

Don't look now there's a monkey on your back
Don't look now there's a monkey on your . . .

So you tell me that you won't do any more
If I keep on asking baby
Maybe I'll get what I'm asking for

Why can't you do it
Why can't you set your monkey free?
Always giving in to it
Do you love the monkey
Or do you love me?
Why can't you do it
Why do I have to share my baby
With a monkey, with a monkey?

Monkey, monkey, monkey
Monkey, monkey, monkey

42 Mother's Pride

Words and Music by George Michael

all the lo-vers gone.__ They make no_____ dif - ference, no____

__ dif-ference in the end. Still__ hear the wo-men say,

__ your Dad-dy died__ a he - ro,_____

in the name of God and man. Mo-ther's pride, cra-zy boy, his

life-less eyes.__ He's a sol - dier now__ for ev - er-more.

He'll hold a gun____ till king-dom come.

And as he grows he hears the band
Takes the step from boy to man
At the shore she waves her son goodbye
Like the man she did before

Mother's pride, just a boy
His country's eyes
He's a soldier waving at the shore
And in her heart
The time has come to lose a son

All the husbands, all the sons
All the lovers gone
They make no difference
No difference in the end
Still hear the women say
Your Daddy died a hero
In the name of God and man

Mother's pride, crazy boy
His lifeless eyes
He's a soldier now for ever more
He'll hold a gun till kingdom come

43 Move On

Words and Music by George Michael

I think of all the days and nights that_ I_____ spent cry - ing_

un - til_____ my_ an - gel set me free._____

repeat ad lib. to fade

I'm

gon-na be luck-y in love some day, ___

I'm gon-na be luck-y in love some day.

I've been in and out of favour with love
Because, I gotta tell ya
I've been things I never wanted to be, mmm
And then some angel called me up
And told me I was sleeping
Don't waste time
'Cause even angels say goodbye

Waiting for that change of season
Ah the winter's been so long
Searching for that rhyme or reason
You've just got to move on
Hold it together, move on
Life's so short, move on
Only time will set you free
Just like me, so move on
You put your fears behind you
I think of all the days and nights
I've spent crying endlessly

And oh there goes another season
Getting hard to find a decent song to play
But oh I guess I've got my reasons
Everybody thinks I'm doing 'A' O.K.
They ought to know by now

Oh that such a thing should make a mock of your life
And don't you think that maybe moving on is good advice?

Move on, I tell you, move on
Hold it together, move on
Life's so short, move on
And life she won't wait for me, move on
Put your fears behind you
You better get yourself where you wanna be
I think of all the days and nights
That I spent crying
Until my angel set me free
I'm gonna be lucky in love some day

44 My Baby Just Cares For Me

Words by Gus Kahn
Music by Walter Donaldson

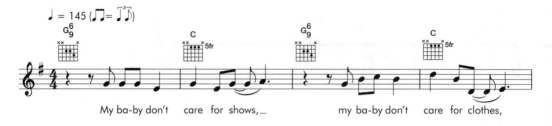

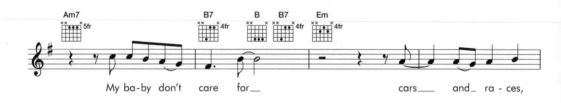

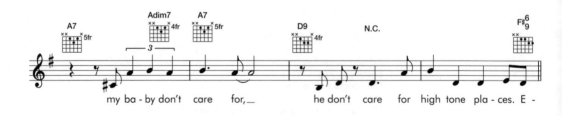

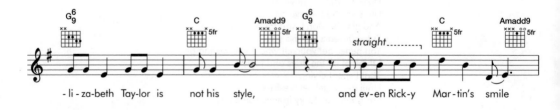

45 Older

Words and Music by George Michael

I should have known, it seemed so easy
You were there, I thought I needed you
Strange, baby
Don't you think I'm looking older
But something good has happened to me
Change is a stranger
Who never seems to show

So you're out of time, I'm letting go
You'll be fine or maybe you won't
You're out of time, I'm letting go
I'm not the man that you want

I never should have looked back
In your direction
I know that
Just the same old fights again baby
There are wasted days
Without affection
I'm not that foolish anymore

So you're out of time, I'm letting go
You'll be fine, well that much I know
You're out of time, I'm letting go
I'm not the man that you want

46　One More Try

Words and Music by George Michael

I've had e-nough of dan - ger and peo-ple on_ the streets,

I'm look-ing out for an - gels just trying to find some peace.

Now I think it's time that you let me know,

so if you love me, say you love me,___ but if you don't, just let me go.___

Chorus

'Cause tea - cher, there are things that I don't want to learn

and the last one I had___ made me cry. So I don't wan-na learn to

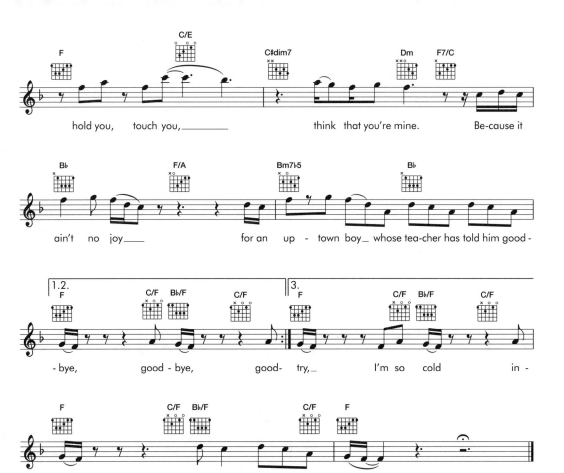

When you were just a stranger
And I was at your feet
I didn't feel the danger
Now I feel the heat
That look in your eyes
Telling me no
So you think that you love me
Know that you need me
I wrote the song, I know it's wrong
Just let me go . . .

And teacher there are things
That I don't want to learn
Oh and the last one I had made me cry
So I don't want to learn to
Hold you, touch you
Think you're mine
Because it ain't no joy
For an uptown boy
Whose teacher has told him goodbye

Instrumental

So when you say that you need me
That you'll never leave me
I know you're wrong
You're not that strong
Let me go

And teacher there are things
That I still have to learn
But the one thing I have is my pride
Oh so I don't want to learn to
Hold you, touch you
Think that you're mine
Because there ain't no joy
For an uptown boy
Who just isn't willing to try
I'm so cold inside
Maybe just one more try

47 Outside

Words and Music by George Michael

take me to the pla-ces that I_____ love best._   And

ba - by._   When the moon is high,__   and the grass is jump-

\- in',   come on,_____   just keep on funk - in'.

Let's go outside
(Let's go outside)
In the sunshine
I know you want to
But you can't say yes
(Let's go outside)
In the meantime
Take me to the places
That I love best

And yes I've been bad
Doctor won't you do with me what you can
You see I think about it all the time
Twentyfour seven

You say you want it, you got it
I never really said it before
There's nothing here, but flesh and bone
There's nothing more, nothing more
There's nothing more
Back to nature, just human nature
Getting on back to . . .

I think I'm done with the sofa
I think I'm done with the hall
I think I'm done with the kitchen table baby

Let's go outside
(Let's go outside)
In the sunshine
I know you want to
But you can't say yes
Let's go outside
(Let's go outside)
In the moonshine
Take me to the places
That I love best

And yes I've been bad
Doctor won't you do with me what you can
You see I think about it all the time
I'd service the community
(But I already have you see!)

I never really said it before
There's nothing here, but flesh and bone
There's nothing more, nothing more
There's nothing more

Let's go outside
Dancing on the D-train baby
When the moon is high
And the grass is jumping
Come on, just keep on funkin'

48 Praying For Time

Words and Music by George Michael

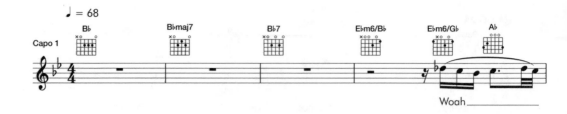

Woah_____

yeah, mm__ do____ oh.____

These are the days of the op-en hand,__ they will not be the last,

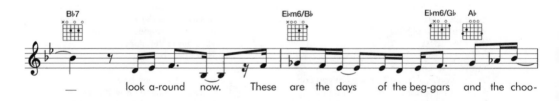

__ look a-round now. These are the days of the beg-gars and the choo-

- sers. This is the year of the hun-gry man__ whose place is in__ the past,

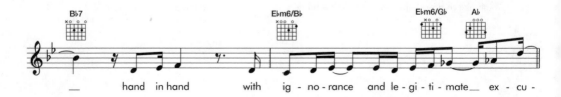

__ hand in hand with ig-no-rance and le-gi-ti-mate__ ex-cu-

- ses.____ The rich de-clare them-selves____ poor,__ and most of us are not

sure____ if we have too much, but we'll take our chan-ces 'cause God's stopped keep-ing

score. I guess some-where a-long the way,____ he must have let us all__ out to play,

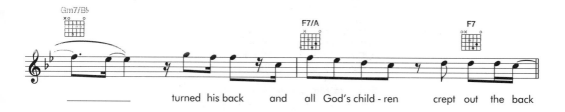

_____ turned his back and all God's child-ren crept out the back

__ door.__ And it's hard to love, there's so much to hate,_____

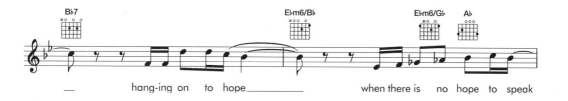

__ hang-ing on to hope_____ when there is no hope to speak

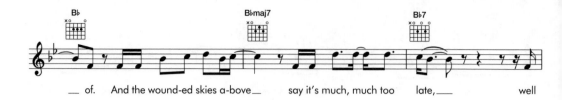

_ of. And the wound-ed skies a-bove_ say it's much, much too late,_ well

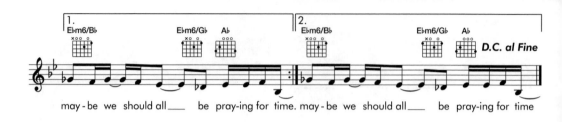

may-be we should all_ be pray-ing for time. may-be we should all_ be pray-ing for time

These are the days of the empty hand
Oh you hold on to what you can
And charity is a coat you wear
Twice a year
This is the year of the guilty man
Your television takes a stand
And you find that what was over there
Is over here

So you scream from behind your door
Say what's mine is mine and not yours
I may have too much
But I'll take my chances
'Cause God stopped keeping score
And you cling to the things they sold
You did cover your eyes when they told you
That he can't come back
'Cause he has no children to come back for

And it's hard to love
There's so much to hate
Hanging on to hope
When there is no hope to speak of
And the wounded skies above
Say it's much too late
So maybe we should all be praying for time

49 Roxanne

Words and Music by Sting

50 Safe

Words and Music by George Michael

Someday, my darkest fears will find their way
After all, somebody loves me, loves me, loves me
All day, my heart tells strangers how I feel
And it's hard not to feel this way
When you thought your future was on prescription

Chorus

Woh, you make me feel safe
Woh, you make me feel safe

51 Secret Love

Words and Music by Sammy Fain and Paul Francis Webster

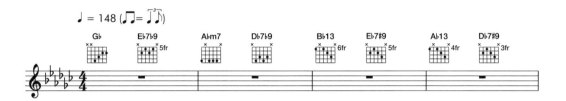

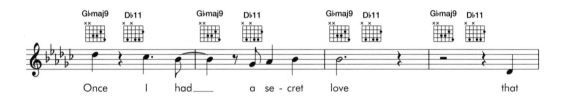

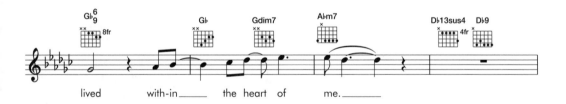

Once I had_ a se-cret love that

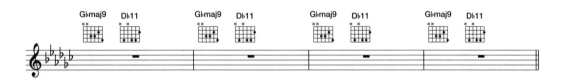

lived with-in_ the heart of me._

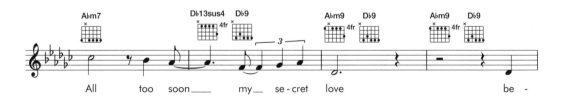

All too soon_ my_ se-cret love be -

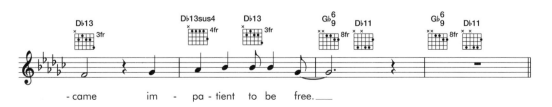

- came im - pa - tient to be free._

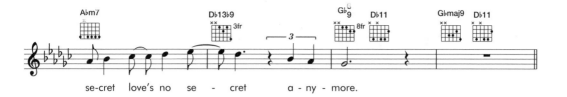

se-cret loves's no se - cret a - ny - more.

D.% al Coda   ⊕ **CODA**

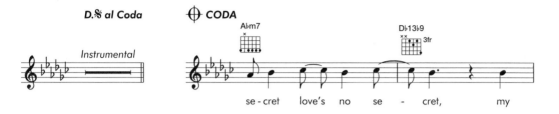

Instrumental

se - cret loves's no se - cret, my

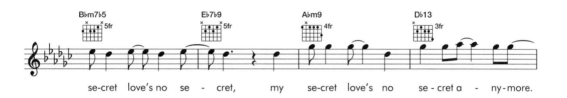

se-cret loves's no se - cret, my se-cret loves's no se - cret a - ny-more.

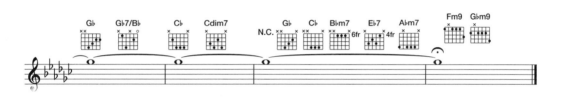

Now I shout it from the highest hills
Even told the golden daffodils
At last my heart's an open door
And my secret love's no secret
My secret love's no secret
My secret love's no secret anymore

52 Somebody To Love

Words and Music by Freddie Mercury

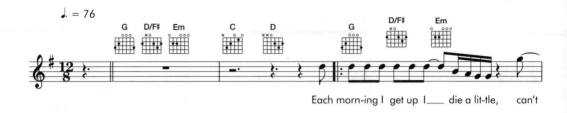

Each morn-ing I get up I___ die a lit-tle, can't

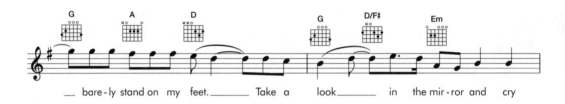

___ bare-ly stand on my feet._____ Take a look_____ in the mir-ror and cry

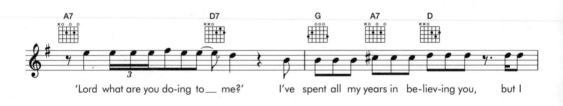

'Lord what are you do-ing to__ me?' I've spent all my years in be-liev-ing you, but I

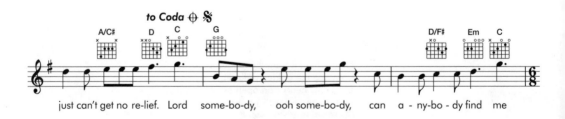

just can't get no re-lief. Lord some-bo-dy, ooh some-bo-dy, can a-ny-bo-dy find me

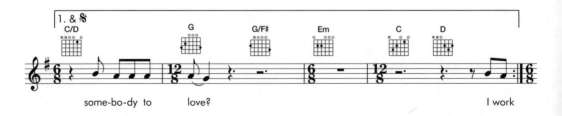

some-bo-dy to love? I work

some-bo - dy to love?

Ev - ery day I try and I try and I try, but ev -
(He works hard ev - ery day.)

- ery-bo-dy wants to put me down, they say I'm go-ing_ cra - zy.__

They say I've got a lot of wa - ter in my brain, ain't got

no com-mon sense. He's got no-bo - dy left to be - lieve in.

D.%% al Coda
Instrumental

CODA

Yeah__ yeah__ yeah__ yeah.__

__

Spoken G5

play 4 times

Find me some-bo-dy to love,_ find me some-bo-dy to love._

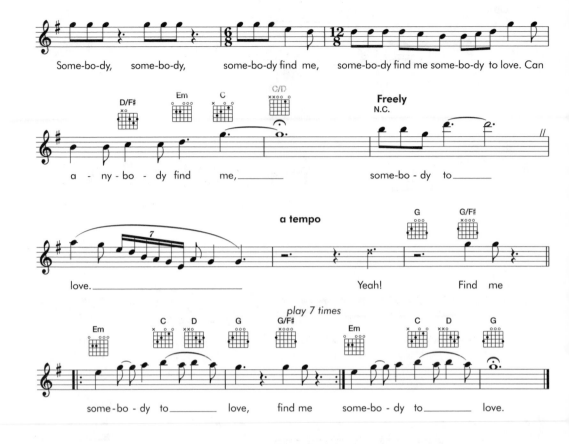

I work hard everyday of my life
I work till i ache my bones
At the end of the day
I take home my hard-earned pay all on my own
I go down on my knees and I start to pray
Till the tears run down from my eyes
Lord somebody (somebody) ooh somebody (somebody)
Can anybody find me somebody to love?

He works hard every day
I try and i try and I try
But everybody wants to put me down
They say I'm going crazy
They say I've got a lot of water in my brain
Ain't got no common sense
He's got nobody left to believe in
Yeah, yeah, yeah, yeah

Instrumental
Ooh somebody, somebody
Can anybody find me somebody to love?

I got no feel, I got no rhythm
I just keep losing my beat
I'm alright, I'm alright
I ain't gonna face no defeat
I just gotta get out of this prison cell
Some day I'm gonna be free, Lord

Find me somebody to love
Find me somebody to love
Somebody, somebody, somebody find me
Somebody find me somebody to love
Can anybody find me somebody to love?
Find me somebody to love

53 Something To Save

Words and Music by George Michael

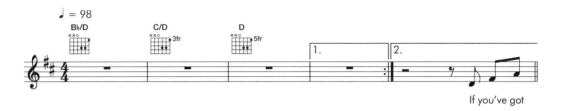

If you've got some-thing to say, why don't you say it?_ If you've got some-thing to give, why don't you

give it_ to me? Day af-ter day I have to say it,_ we're mov-ing

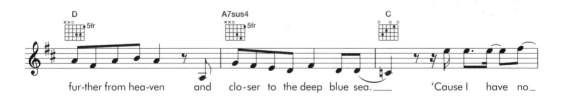

fur-ther from hea-ven and clo-ser to the deep blue sea._ 'Cause I have no_

_ se-crets from you,_ and I have no - thing left to hide_

Like I_____ have._____

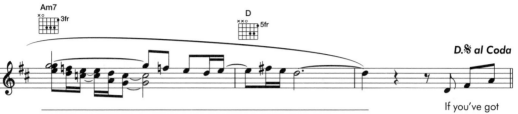

D.℠ al Coda

If you've got

⊕ CODA

some-thing to save, why don't we save_____ it?_____

And all these games that you play
Don't tell me how a man should be
Some would say if you knew
You wouldn't be here with me
(With me)
I love you
(I love you)
I still love you
(I still love you)
But I guess it's time to let you be
'Cause I have no secrets from you
And I have nothing left to hide
And I'm so tired of all these questions
'Cause maybe you just changed your mind
Like I have, like I have

When I was at your doorstep
You told me to look around
Said come in, you and your heart sit down
But you better watch your step
'Cause you're not far from the ground
And one fine day this all falls down
Like I have

If you've got something to say
Why don't you say it?
If you've got something to give
Why don't you give it to me?
Day after day, I have to say it
If we've got something to save
Why don't we save it?

54 Soul Free

Words and Music by George Michael

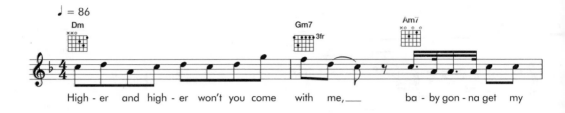

High - er and high - er won't you come with me, ___ ba - by gon - na get my

soul ___ free, ___ soul ___ free. ___

High - er and high - er won't you come with me, ___ ba - by gon - na get my

soul ___ free, ___ soul ___ free. ___

Instrumental on %

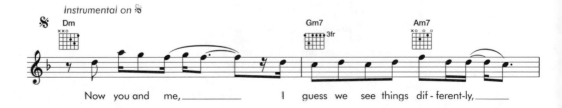

Now you and me, ___ I guess we see things dif - ferent-ly, ___

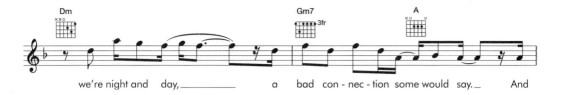

we're night and day,_____ a bad con-nec-tion some would say._ And

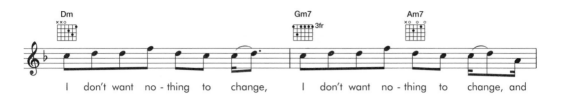

I don't want no-thing to change, I don't want no-thing to change, and

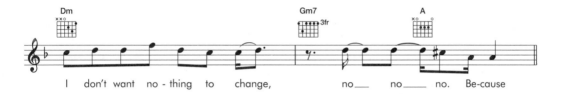

I don't want no-thing to change, no_ no_ no. Be-cause

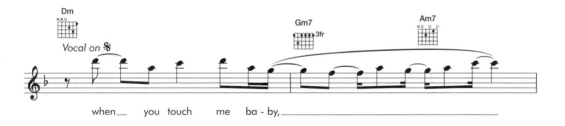

Vocal on 𝄋

when_ you touch me ba-by,_____

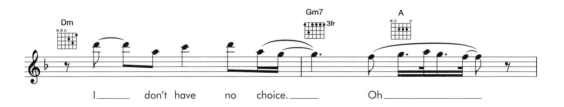

I_____ don't have no choice._____ Oh_____

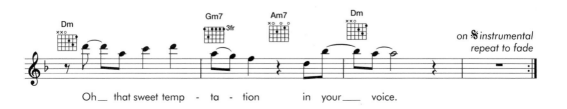

on 𝄋 instrumental
repeat to fade

Oh_ that sweet temp-ta-tion in your_ voice.

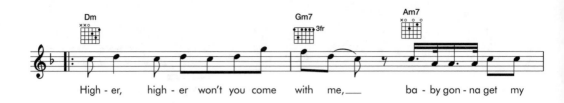

High - er, high - er won't you come with me, ___ ba - by gon - na get my

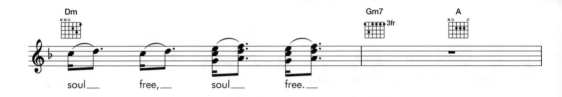

soul ___ free, ___ soul ___ free. ___

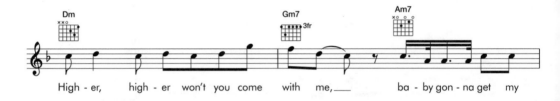

High - er, high - er won't you come with me, ___ ba - by gon - na get my

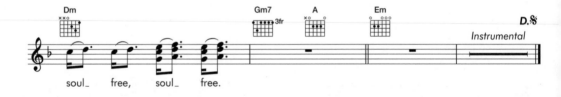

Instrumental

D.%

soul_ free, soul_ free.

Higher, higher won't you come with me
Baby gonna get my soul free, soul free

Now seems to me
Some things have just got to be
The games we play
Make up, break up day by day
And I don't want nothing to change
I don't want nothing to change
I don't want nothing to change
Said I don't want nothing to change
No, no, no because

When you touch me baby
I don't have no choice
Oh that sweet temptation in your voice

Higher, higher won't you come with me
Baby gonna get my soul free, soul free

When you touch me baby
I don't have no choice
Oh that sweet temptation in your voice

55 Spinning The Wheel

Words and Music by George Michael and Johnny Douglas

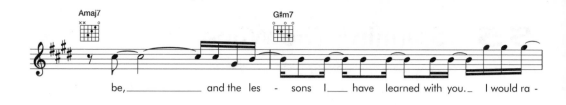

be,_____ and the les - sons I___ have learned with you._ I would ra -

- ther be__ a - lone_ than watch you spin - ning that wheel for me.

_ You've got a thing a-bout dan-ger, ain't you get-ting what you want from me?

You've got a thing a-bout stran-gers ba-by, that's what we used to be._____

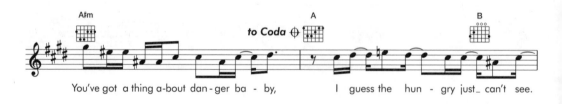

You've got a thing a-bout dan - ger ba - by, I guess the hun - gry just_ can't see.

_ One of these days you're gon-na bring some home to me. __

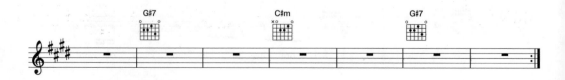

I'm ne-ver go-ing back to that, and that's a fact ba - by!

One of these days you're gon-na bring some home to _____ me,

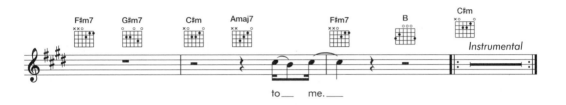

to___ me.___

Instrumental

Six o'clock in the morning
You ain't phoned
I can't help thinking that's strange yeah, yeah
It seems that everybody takes their chances
These days, oh yeah
We're standing in the rain
And I will not accept this as
A part of my life
I will not live in fear of what may be
And the lessons I have learned with you
I would rather be alone than watch you
Spinning that wheel for me

You've got a thing about danger
Ain't you getting what you want from me
You've got a thing about strangers baby
That's what we used to be
You've got a thing about danger baby
I guess the hungry just can't see
One of these days you're gonna bring some home to me

How can you love me
When you're playing with my life
Give me time and I'll do better I swear
Give me time and I'll lead you back to despair
And I don't want to go back there
I don't want to go back there
I'm never going back to that
And that's a fact baby!
One of these days you're gonna bring some home to me

56 Star People

Words and Music by George Michael

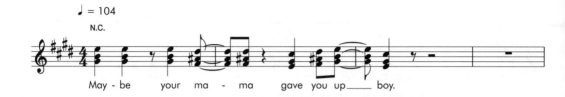

May - be   your ma - ma   gave you up____ boy.

May - be   your dad - dy did-n't love you e - nough   girl. _

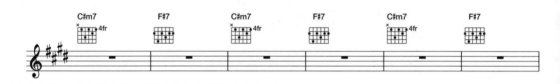

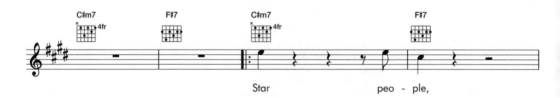

Star   peo - ple,

count-ing your mon-ey un - til your soul   turns green.   Star   peo -

- ple,____   count-ing the cost_ of your de - si - re to be__ seen.

CODA

talk a - bout_ the peo - ple who have paid for that new sports car._

_ Mm_ ah_____ ah, ah, ah,_____ ah. You're a big_

_ big big_ bad star._ Look at you.

1–3. **4.**

Say how much is e-nough? much is e-nough?
How much is e-nough?

Star people never forget
Your secret's safe with me
Just look at all the wonderful people
Trying to forget they had to pay
For what you see
It's a dream with a nightmare
Stuck in the middle
But listen brother
Where would you be
Without all of this attention?
You'd die, I'd die
We'd die wouldn't we?
Well wouldn't we?

You're a star
(Ooh I'm talking to you)
You're a star

I said maybe your mama gave you up boy
It's the same old same old
Maybe your daddy didn't love you enough girl

You only wanted them to love you
You may have been living in a dream
And as the demons tower above you
You bite your tongue
When you really want to scream

Talk about your mother
Talk about your father
Talk about the people
Who have made you what you are
Talk about your teacher
The bully boy who beat you
Talk about the people who have paid
For that new sports car

Mm ah ah ah ah ah
You're a big, big, big, bad star
Look at you
Say how much is enough
(How much is enough)
Did you get off on a bad foot baby?
Do you have a little tale to tell?
Did you get off on a bad foot, a bad, a bad foot?
Is that why you're a star?
Is that what makes a star?
Say how much is enough?
(How much is enough?)
Did you get off on a bad foot baby?
Do you have a little tale to tell?
Say how much is enough?
(How much is enough)
Well nothing comes from nothing baby
That fame and fortune's heaven sent
And who gives a fuck about your problems darling
'Cause you can pay the rent?
How much is enough?

57 The Strangest Thing

Words and Music by George Michael

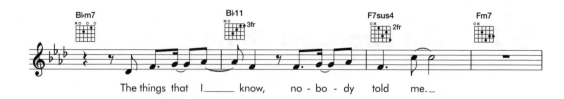

The things that I_____ know, no-bo-dy told me.___

The seeds that are___ sown, they still con-trol____ me._____ There's a

li-ar in___ my___ head,___ there's a thief up-on___ my___ bed.___ And the

D.C.

strang-est___ thing, ___ is I can-not seem to___ get____ my eyes off

La___ la la la___ la la la___ la___ la. La___ la la la___ la la la___ la___ la.

to Coda

La la la la. ___

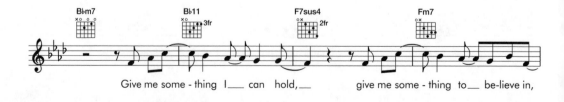

Give me some-thing I___ can hold, ___ give me some-thing to___ be-lieve in,

I am fright - ened for— my soul.— Please, please make

— love to— me, send— love through me, heal me with your cry.___ The on -

- ly one_ who ev - er knew me, we've wast - ed so_ much time,___ so much

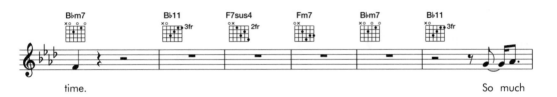

time. So much

D.% *al Coda* **⊕ CODA**

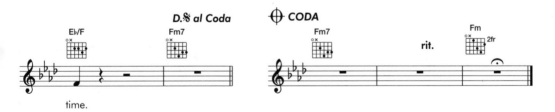

time.

rit.

Take my hand
Lead me to some peaceful land
That I cannot find
Inside my head
Wake me with love
It's all, all I need
But in all this time
Still no-one says
If I had not asked
Would you have told me
If you call this love
Why don't you hold me

There's a liar in my head
There's a thief up on my bed
And the strangest thing
Is I cannot seem to get my eyes off you

Give me something I can hold
Give me something I can believe in
I am frightened for my soul
Please, please make love to me
Send love to me
Send love through me

Heal me with your cry
The only one who ever knew me
We've wasted so much time

There's a liar in my head
There's a thief up on my bed
And the strangest thing
Is I cannot seem to get my eyes off you

The only one who ever knew me
We've wasted so much time
So much time

58   These Are The Days Of Our Lives

Words and Music by Queen

Some-times I get to feel-in' I was back in the old days, long a-go,

when_ we were kids, when_ we were young, things seemed

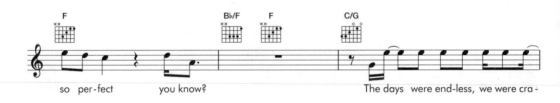

so per-fect you know? The days were end-less, we were cra -

- zy, we were young, the sun was al-ways shin-in', we just lived for fun._

Some-times it seems like late - ly, I just don't know, the rest of my life's____ been

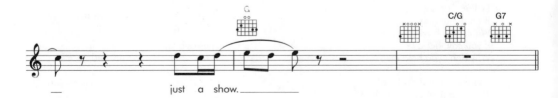

____ just a show._____

You can't turn back the clock
You can't turn back the tide
Ain't that a shame?
I'd like to go back one time
On a roller coaster ride
When life's just a game

No use in sitting
And a-thinking on what you did
When you can lay back and enjoy it
Through your kids
Sometimes it seems like lately
I just don't know
Better sit back
And go with the flow

These are the days of our lives
They've flown in the swiftness of time
Those days are all gone now
But some things remain
When I look
I find no change

Those were the days of our lives
The bad things in life were so few
Those days are all gone now
But one thing's still true
When I look and I find
I still love you

59   They Won't Go When I Go

Words and Music by Stevie Wonder and Yvonne Wright

No more ly - ing friends want-ing tra - gic_ ends, though they do_ pre - tend,

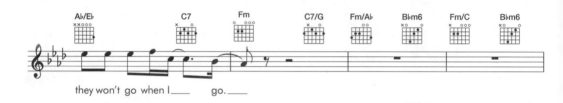

they won't go when I___ go.___

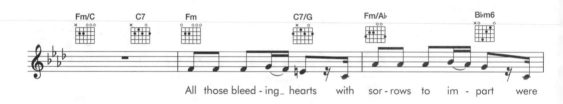

All those bleed - ing_ hearts with sor - rows to im - part were

right here from the start, they won't go when I___ go.___ And I'll

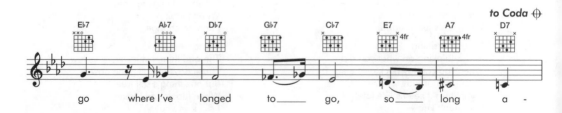

go where I've longed to___ go, so___ long a -

take more_____ than he will give,_____ he will give,_____

he will give,_____ he ain't hard-ly gon-na give._ Wo_____ yeah._

D.C. al Coda

The

✛ CODA

from_____ my___ des - ti - ny. _____

Gone from painful cries
Away from saddened eyes
Along with him I'll bide
They won't go when I go

Big men feeling small
Weak ones standing tall
I will watch them fall
They won't go when I go

And I'll go where I've longed to go
So long away from tears

Unclean minds mislead the pure
The innocent will leave for sure
For them there is a resting place
People sinning just for fun
They will never see the sun

For they can never show their faces
There ain't no room for the hopeless sinner
Who will take more than he will give
He will give, he will give
He ain't hardly gonna give, wo yeah

The greed of man will be
Far away from me
And my soul will be free
They won't go when I go

Since my soul conceived
All that I believe
The kingdom I will see
They won't go when I go

And I go where I'll go
No-one can keep me
From my destiny

60 To Be Forgiven

Words and Music by George Michael

I'm go-ing down, won't you help___ me? (Won't you help___ me now?) Save

___ me from___ my - self.___

I hear the sound of a me - mo-ry,___ may-

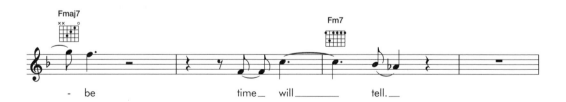

- be time___ will_____ tell.___

Sud-den - ly my life___ is like___ a ri - ver,___

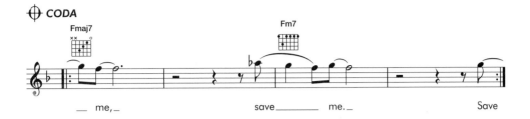

CODA

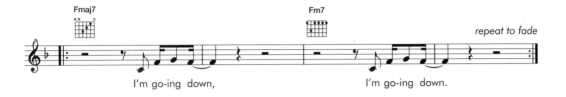

_ me,_   save_____ me._   Save

Fmaj7   Fm7   *repeat to fade*

I'm go-ing down,   I'm go-ing down.

I'm going down
Won't you help me?
(Won't you help me now?)
Save me from myself
I look around for a fantasy
Maybe, who can tell

Let me live my life
Beside the river
Take me to places
Where a child can grow
And then maybe, maybe
The boy inside me
Will forsake me
Maybe the child in me
Will just let me go

Instrumental

I'm going down
Cold, cold water
is rushing in
I'm going down
And I would beg
To be forgiven
If I knew myself
If I knew myself
Save me, save me
I'm going down
I'm going down

61 Too Funky

Words and Music by George Michael

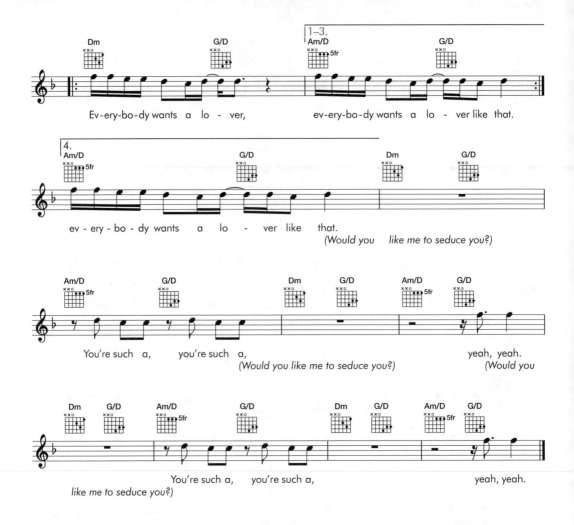

Hey you're just too funky for me
I've got to get inside of you
And I'll show you heaven if you'll let me
Hey you're just too funky for me
I've got to get inside
I've got to get inside of you

I watch you drinking and I take my time
I watch you sinking all that cheap red wine
I've got to see you naked baby
I'd like to think that sometime
Maybe tonight my goal's in sight

Baby, baby, baby, why do you do this to me?
Won't let you go
You're such a, you're such a
Baby, baby, baby, why do you do this to me?
I've got to know

(Gonna be the kind of lover that you never had)
Hey you're just too funky
(You're never gonna have another lover in your bed)
You're just too funky for me

(Would you like me to seduce you?
Is that what you're trying to tell me?)
Everybody wants a lover like that
Everybody wants a lover like that
(Is that what you're trying to tell me?)
Everybody wants a lover
Everybody wants a lover like that
Everybody wants a lover
Everybody wants a lover like that
(Would you like me to seduce you?)
You're such a, you're such a
(Would you like me to seduce you?)

Spoken
Would you stop playing with that radio of yours
I'm trying to get to sleep

62 Waiting For That Day

Words and Music by George Michael

So ev-ery day_ I see_ you in_ some oth-er_ face,_____ they

crack a smile,_ talk a while, try to take your place._____ Mm, my

me-mo-ry_____ serves me far_____ too well._____ I_

__ just sit_ here on_ this moun-tain think-ing to_ my-self,_____ you're a fool

__ boy, why don't you go_ down find_____ some-bo - dy, find some-bo - dy else._

_____ My_____ me-mo-ry_____ serves me far_____ too well.

It's not as_ though_____ we just broke up,_____

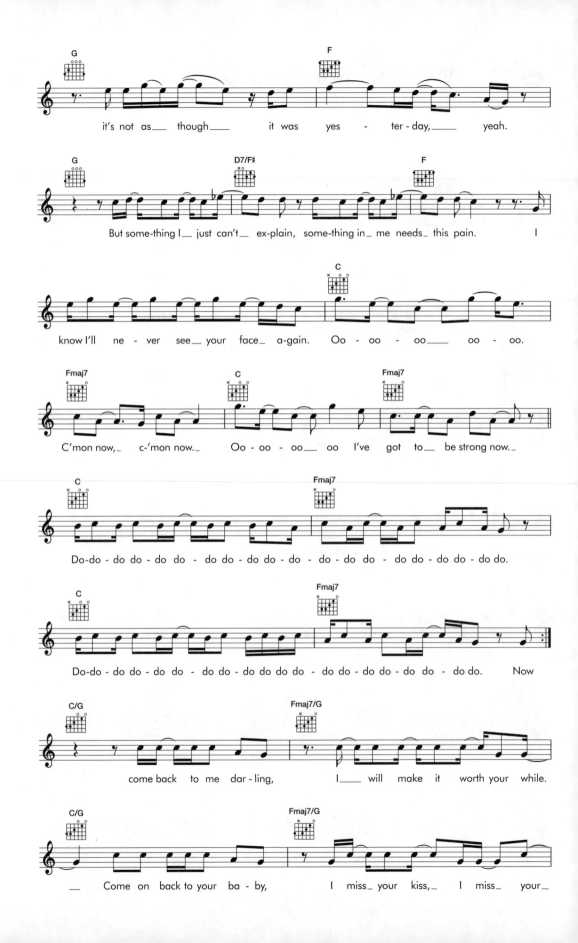

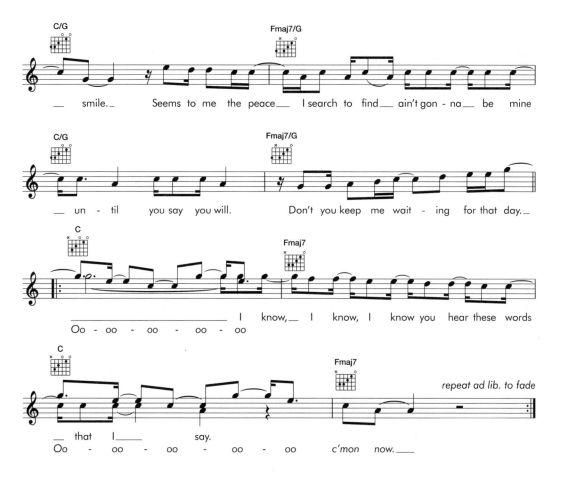

Now everybody's talking about this new decade
Like you say the magic numbers
Then just say goodbye to the stupid mistakes you made
Oh my memory serves me far too well
Don't you know that the years will come and go
Some of us will change our lives
Some of us still have nothing to show
Nothing baby but memories

And if these wounds they are self inflicted
I don't really know how
My poor heart could have protected me
But if I have to carry this pain
If you will not share the blame
I deserve to see your face again

C'mon now, c'mon now
You don't have to be so strong
Come back, come back
Come back, come back
Come back to me darling
I will make it worth your while
Come back to your baby
I miss your kiss, I miss your smile
Seems to me the peace I search to find
Ain't gonna be mine until you say you will
Don't you keep me waiting for that day
I know, I know, I know
You hear these words that I say
C'mon now

You can't always get what you want

63 Waiting (Reprise)

Words and Music by Dennis Morgan and Simon Climie

There ain't___ no point___ in mov - ing on___ till you've

got some-where to go._____ And the road that I___ have walked up-on, well it

filled my poc-kets and emp-tied out___ my___ (Do do do - do-do) (Do-do
soul.

do do do - do-do) (Do-do do do do - do-do) (Do-do

do do do - do-do) All those in - se - cu - ri - ties___ that have

held me down for so long.__ I can't say that I've found a cure for these, but at

least I know them so they're not so strong. You look for your dreams in hea-ven, but what the hell

64 Waltz Away Dreaming

Words and Music by George Michael and Toby Bourke

She's got a song in her head and she'll sing to me.

She's got a laugh that re-minds me of why___ she's in

love with me. She'd ne-ver let show she was lone-ly in case it had

fright-tened me. She was car-pet and stone, in-de-pen-dent, a-lone, but this

1.

love al-ways shone a-round me___ ev-ery time.___

Chorus

Waltz a-way___ dream-ing till your day be-gins a-gain.___

love.__ (You see me,__ I will live in__ your life, we will
mo - ment_ you

walk through your gar - den,__ I will see through your eyes.) Ev - ery

G.M.
She had a history of joy and pain in time
And she chose to leave
She had a thousand and one photographs
That you would not believe
She'll come to you in disguise
She's there in your children's eyes
Still our mother . . .she's still your wife
(So let her . . .

Both
Waltz away dreaming
Till your day begins once again
Free from the reasons
And this state I'm in
T.B.
And oh
G.M.
Trust me, she ain't going nowhere
T.B.
I can't hold it all under one love
G.M.
Trust me, she told me
When you're ready she'll be there
T.B.
It was so long ago
G.M.
No don't go of her
Both
When we kissed in the streets
Now you fly like an eagle above
While I waltz away anyway
Then I'm waltzing my days away
Searching for this woman I love

(And the moment you see me
I will live in your life
We will walk through my garden
I will see through your eyes)
T.B.
Waltz away dreaming
G.M.
I was in despair till she found me there
Every grown man cries with his mother's eyes
And when you're ready too
She'll come back to you
She's waiting
T.B.
Waltzing my days away
G.M.
. . .Father . . .she's waiting

65 Where Or When

Words by Lorenz Hart
Music by Richard Rodgers

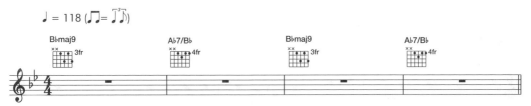

It seems we stood and talked like this____ be - fore.

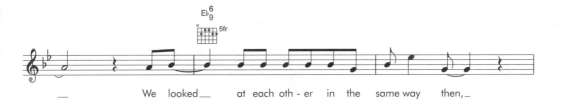

_ We looked____ at each oth - er in the same way then,_

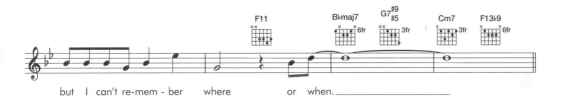

but I can't re-mem - ber where or when.____

The clothes you're wear-ing are the clothes____ you wore.

_ The smile____ that you are smil-ing you were smil-ing then,_

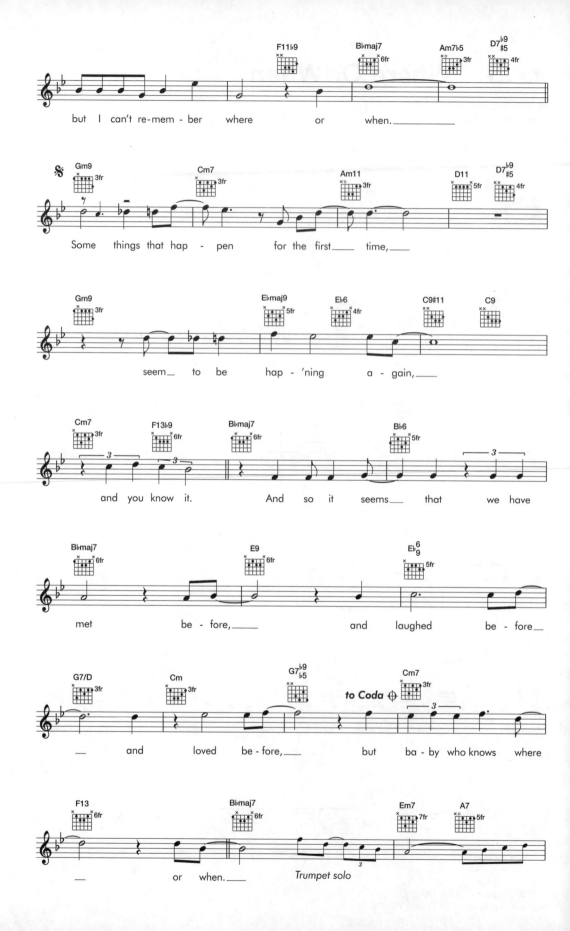

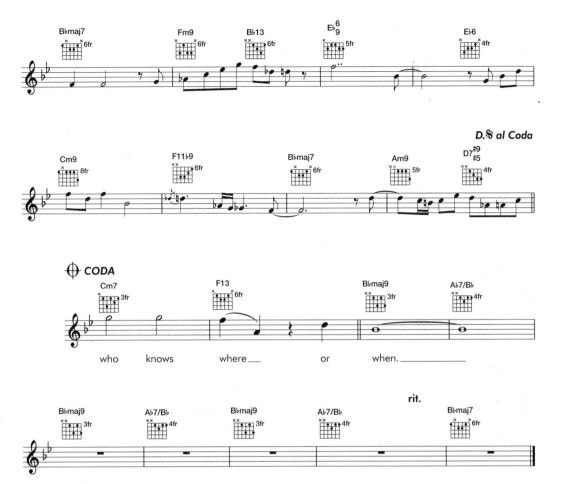

who   knows   where___   or   when._____

Some things that happen for the first time
Seem to be happening again
And so it seems that we have met before
And laughed before and loved before
But who knows where or when

66 Wild Is The Wind

Words by Ned Washington
Music by Dimitri Tiomkin

Love me, love me, love me, say_____ you do. Let me

fly_____ a - way_____ with you, for my love is like_____ the wind,

and wild_____ is the wind. Give me more than

one_____ ca - ress,_____ sa - tis - fy this hun - gri-ness.

Let the wind blow through your heart,_____ and wild_____

is the wind._____ You__ touch me,_____

67 You Have Been Loved

Words and Music by George Michael and David Austin

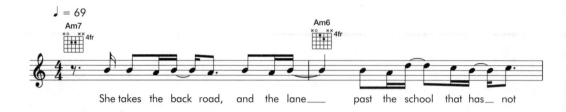

She takes the back road, and the lane___ past the school that has___ not

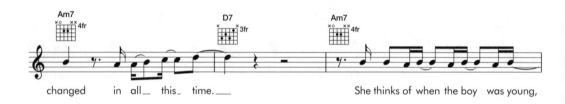

changed in all___ this___ time.___ She thinks of when the boy was young,

___ all the bat - tles she_ had___ won, just___ to give_ him life._

___ That man, she loved that_ man,___ for all his_ life._

___ And now we meet to take him flo - wers, and on - ly God knows

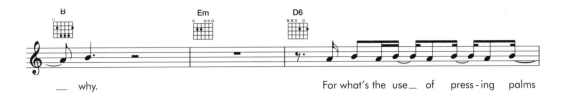

_ why.   For what's the use_ of press-ing palms

_ when child-ren fade_ in mo-ther's arms?_____ It's a cruel world, we've

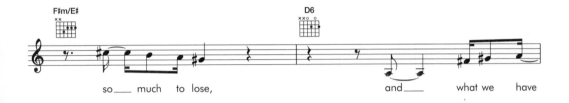

so_ much to lose,   and_ what we have

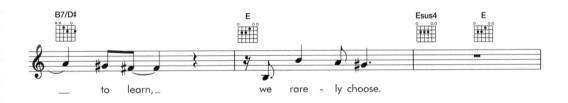

_ to learn,_   we rare-ly choose.

So if it's God who took her son,   he can-not be_ the one

_ liv-ing in_ her_____ mind.   'Take care_ my love,'

she said,   'Don't think__   that God____ is dead'.

'Take care__   my love,'__ she said,_____   'You have__ been loved.'

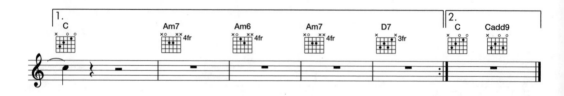

If I was weak, forgive me
But I was terrified
You brushed my eyes with angels' wings
Full of love
The kind that makes devils cry
So these days my life has changed
And I'll be fine
But she just sits and counts the hours
Searching for her crime

So what's the use in pressing palms
If you won't keep such love from harm?
It's a cruel world, you've so much to prove
And heaven help the ones who wait for you

Now I've no daughters, I've no sons
Guess I'm the only one living in my life
'Take care my love' he said
'Don't think that God is dead'
'Take care my love' he said
'You have been loved'

68 You Know That I Want To

Words and Music by George Michael and Jonathan Douglas

Lo-ver, don't love too much,_ it's a bad_ thing, a sad

_ thing and it's hea-ven_ to the touch._____ Hey, ev-ery-

- bo-dy's got_ some mo-ment in_ their lives,_ they can't___ change,____

don't they_ ba - by._ I know you don't_ care

what's right_____ or_ wrong. All___ that I know

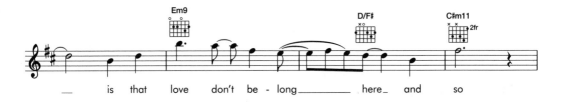

_ is that love don't be-long_____ here_ and so

So it hap - pens ev - ery time, it's so

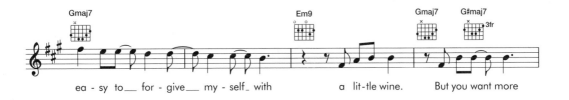

ea - sy to__ for - give__ my - self_ with a lit-tle wine. But you want more

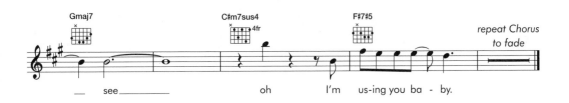

and the plea - sure will__ be all___ mine.__ Can't you

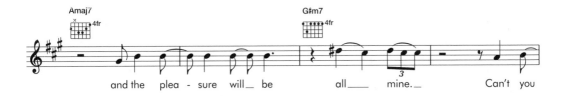

repeat Chorus
to fade

__ see_____ oh I'm us-ing you ba - by.

Lover don't love too much
I'm a bad boy, I'm a sad boy
And I never give you much
Everybody's got some moment in their lives
They can't change
So I do not dare to take you home
All that I know is
There's something so wrong with this heat
Why do you touch the flame?
You only feel the pain my dear
You always find it here
But you say

Chorus
I can't stop but you know that I want to
I can't stop don't you know that I want you
I want you baby, more than ever
I can't stop but you know that I want to
I can't stop don't you know that I want you
But it's never gonna be

So it happens every time
It's so easy to forgive myself with a little wine
But you want more
And the the pleasure will be all mine
Can't you see, I'm using you baby

Repeat Chorus to fade

69 You've Changed

Words by Bill Carey
Music by Carl Fischer

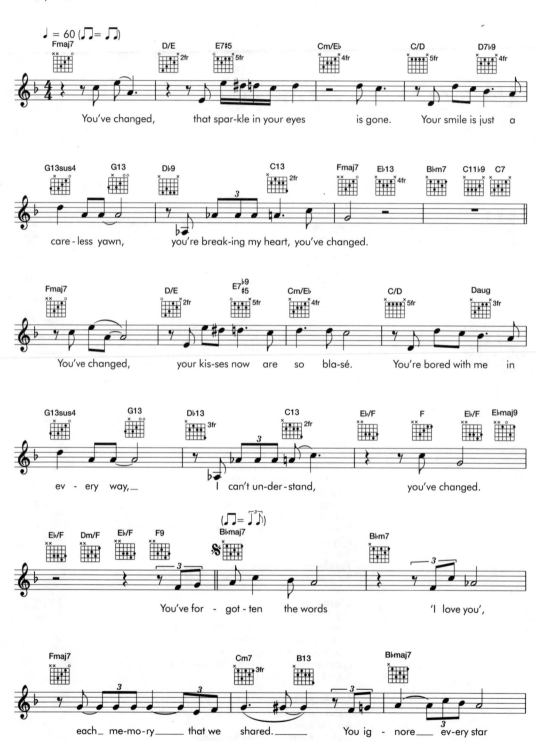

You've forgotten the words 'I love you'
Each memory that we shared
You ignore every star above you
I can't realise you ever cared

You've changed
You're not the angel I once knew
No need to tell me that we're through
It's all over now
You've changed
I miss you

the **INDEX**

INDEX

As – 1

Brother Can You Spare A Dime? – 2

Calling You – 3
Careless Whisper – 4
Cowboys And Angels – 5
Crazyman Dance – 6

Desafinado – 7
A Different Corner – 8
Do You Really Want To Know – 9
Don't Let The Sun Go
　　Down On Me – 10

Everything She Wants – 11

Faith – 12
Fastlove – 13
Fantasy – 14
Father Figure – 15
The First Time Ever I Saw
　　Your Face – 16
Free – 17
Freedom – 18
Freedom '90 – 19

Hand To Mouth – 20
Happy – 21
Hard Day – 22
Heal The Pain – 23

I Believe (When I Fall In Love
　　It Will Be Forever) – 24

I Can't Make You Love Me – 25
I Knew You Were Waiting
　　(For Me) – 26
I Remember You – 27
I Want Your Sex (Part I 'Lust') – 28
I Want Your Sex (Part II) – 29
I Want Your Sex (Part III
　　'A Last Request') – 30
I'm Your Man – 31
If You Were My Woman – 32
It Doesn't Really Matter – 33
It's Alright With Me – 34

Jesus To A Child – 35

Killer/Papa Was A Rolling Stone – 36
Kissing A Fool – 37

Look At Your Hands – 38

Miss Sarajevo – 39
A Moment With You – 40
Monkey – 41
Mother's Pride – 42
Move On – 43
My Baby Just Cares For Me – 44

Older – 45
One More Try – 46
Outside – 47

Praying For Time – 48

Roxanne – 49

Safe – 50
Secret Love – 51
Somebody To Love – 52
Something To Save – 53
Soul Free – 54
Spinning The Wheel – 55
Star People – 56
The Strangest Thing – 57

These Are The Days
    Of Our Lives – 58
They Won't Go When I Go – 59
To Be Forgiven – 60
Too Funky – 61

Waiting For That Day – 62
Waiting (Reprise) – 63
Waltz Away Dreaming – 64
Where Or When – 65
Wild Is The Wind – 66

You Have Been Loved – 67
You Know That I Want To – 68
You've Changed – 69

INGRAF s.r.l. - Via Monte S. Genesio 7 - Milano
Stampato in Italia - Printed in Italy - Imprimé en Italie 2000